AN SAT VOCABULARY NOVEL

BY LYNNE HANSEN

SPARK
NOTES

by Lynne Hansen

SPARKNOTES is a registered trademark of SparkNotes LLC

Spark Publishing
A Division of Barnes & Noble Publishing
120 Fifth Avenue
New York, NY 10011
www.sparknotes.com

SAT is a registered trademark of the College Entrance Examination Board, which was not involved in the production of, and does not endorse, this book.

ISBN-13: 978-1-4114-0440-3
ISBN-10: 1-4114-0440-8

Please submit all questions or comments or report errors to
www.sparknotes.com/errors

Printed and bound in the United States

Library of Congress Cataloging-in-Publication Data available upon request

Rave New World

As teen cyberpsychic Jaden Emory entered the Tamlando Detention Center, he pulled his crocheted cap down over his dreadlocks so that it covered his **gleaming** cybernetic implants. A sea of police officers and addicts stood between him and the addiction cells on the far side of the complex.

"Time to get to work," Jaden muttered, blowing air out of his mouth and stepping into the gray maze of corridors. A slim redhead in a lemon-colored jogging suit with her hands cuffed together in front of her slipped him a shy smile.

Instinctively he smiled back, flashing her his trademark **insouciant** grin. Jaden's tall, lanky frame, huge, white-boy dreads, and big, glossy brown eyes tended to get him noticed.

By girls in particular.

Jaden wiped the cocky smile off his face, **abashed**. What had he been thinking? This girl might just be "noticing" him, but she might also be smiling because she remembered him from his past. His somewhat *shady* past. Well, not to put too fine a point on it, his one-more-strike-and-we're-locking-you-up-and-throwing-away-the-key past.

He picked up his pace, ambling forward a little faster and letting his breath out.

As his team leader, Kim could make him come to the T.D.C., but she couldn't make him **linger**. He'd pop in, do his job, and leave. He'd only stay long enough to split away the addict's **vice**, then he was out of there.

When he finally paused outside addiction cell #642, **trepidation** gave way to anticipation. His fingers tingled as he removed

---

gleaming: shining
insouciant: nonchalant or untroubled

abashed: embarrassed
linger: hang around

vice: moral failing or fault
trepidation: fear or apprehension

his cap and stuffed it into the back pocket of his jeans. Who would be waiting for him behind that door?

Back at the Splitter Center, where he lived and handled his run-of-the-mill assignments, he'd probably be facing forty-five minutes with some mom addicted to Twinkies who'd been turned in by a caring family member concerned about her carbohydrate obsession. Here at the Tamlando Detention Center, he was probably facing a violent offender. An alcoholic, perhaps, or a drug addict. He rubbed his palms on his jeans. Kim knew he **abhorred** coming down to the T.D.C., so it had to be a tough case, something she only trusted to him. If he were lucky, maybe he'd get to split a sex addict, or even a psychopath who killed for his addiction. Just beyond that door, guards were probably poised to strike with blast-cannons at the offender's first false move.

God, the year 2157 was stupid.

Well, time to find out.

Jaden exhaled **audibly** and passed his hand over the security lock. The door whooshed open.

Jaden frowned. No burly guards. No state-of-the-art firepower. Just a blue-haired teenage girl and her parents.

The girl **brooded** over the pink laces on her bright orange shoes, carefully avoiding the stern gazes of the scowling couple that flanked her like skyscrapers.

Her scraggly blueberry-colored pigtails bounced when she looked up. Jaden saw a spark of recognition in her eyes, then a flash of **dread**.

As soon as he saw her face, he felt just as **distressed** himself. But he had a **compelling** reason to be upset by her presence here— why should she care about seeing him again?

Jaden ambled forward and extended his hand. "Hey, good to see you again, Ally," he lied. It hadn't even been three weeks ago that he'd cured the **vivacious** raver of her music addiction. Any splitter

---

abhorred: hated
audibly: able to be heard
brooded: thought gloomily about

dread: fear or anxiety
distressed: upset

compelling: forceful or convincing
vivacious: lively

who was at all **adroit** would only require a single session to cure a patient. Since he was thirteen, none of Jaden's patients had required second treatments. Five perfect years, and now this.

Ally **furrowed** her brow in mock confusion. "Um, have we met or something?" she asked, shaking his hand without getting up. Jaden sensed that if she had tried to get up, her mother's well-manicured claw would have come down on her shoulder.

"Uh, whoa, I think—," Jaden began.

Ally's aqua eyes **beseeched** him to **corroborate** her pretense of **ignorance**. Jaden had no idea why she didn't want him to talk about their previous session, but this was fine by him. The last thing he needed right now was The Corporation giving him static about a **recidivist** showing up.

"Oh, sorry. I thought so at first, but you just look a lot like someone I used to know," said Jaden.

Ally perked up. "Was she cute?"

Ally's father **interceded**. "Alan Fayre," he said. He shook Jaden's hand **perfunctorily**, looking with disapproval at Jaden's mammoth mane of dreadlocks, then wiped his hand on his expensive suit. Ally's mother looked on, a pained expression of **exasperation** pressed into her delicate features. Mr. Fayre didn't introduce her.

"Can we just get on with this? I'd like to have her fixed before the press catches wind of her arrest. We're from Upper Management, you know."

"Oh, yeah, no problem, bro," Jaden said, noting how Ally's father talked about her as if she wasn't even in the room. "Let me just **peruse** your file a moment, Miss . . . Ally." He brushed his hand across one of the empty white walls and the wall turned into a computer terminal that allowed him to pull up Ally's record. "Got busted at a rave last night, huh? Was it killer?"

"Uh, *yeah*?" Ally said, her tone implying that it was a stupid question.

---

adroit: skillful
furrowed: made lined or wrinkled
beseeched: pleaded with
corroborate: confirm

ignorance: lack of knowledge
recidivist: person who relapses
interceded: came between to resolve a difference

perfunctorily: mechanically or unenthusiastically
exasperation: extreme annoyance
peruse: read over casually

Ally's mother cleared her throat.

Ally's gaze darted toward the sound. "I mean yes, Splitter—"

"Emory," Jaden finished for her. "You can just call me Jaden if you want, though," he said, smiling. At eighteen, he was only older than Ally by a year, tops, and it didn't feel right for her to call him by his formal title, especially not on their second meeting.

Mr. Fayre sighed. "Well, 'just Jaden,' or 'dude,' or whatever you call yourself according to the **stunted argot** you teenagers speak, can you fix her or not?"

"Uh, your daughter's not broken, Mr. Fayre. She just needs a little extra help in the willpower department." Jaden was beginning to seriously dislike Mr. Fayre. "Uh, so if you'll both be *leaving*, I can get started right away." He presented the door with a **flourish**.

Ally's parents took one last disapproving look at his hair and huffed out.

The second the door slid shut, Ally **bolted** from her chair and started pacing the room nervously. "Man, you're good. They totally bought that. Thanks for not narcing on me. Though I guess that's pretty **ironic**, considering that you actually *are* a cybernarc." Her blue pigtails bounced in time with her **frenetic** motions.

"Um, I beg your pardon, Miss," Jaden began. The Corporation frequently monitored the splitting rooms, and the last thing he needed was for some auditor to overhear their conversation and show up on his doorstep.

"I mean, thanks for telling them we hadn't met before, you goofball," Ally said.

"But we haven't." Jaden winked at her from under his mop of dreads.

Ally rolled her eyes. "Trying to teach me a lesson, I see. What else should I expect from a cybernarc?"

"Um, I think if we could just focus on the reason you're here, which I believe is to help you leave behind this time-wasting, unpro-

---

stunted: not fully grown
argot: secret slang
flourish: showy movement

bolted: moved suddenly
ironic: opposite of the literal meaning

frenetic: frenzied or frantic

ductive addiction you have to music?" Jaden rolled his eyes at the sound of his own voice. He tried to sound **ingenuous**, spouting the corporate script he'd been trained to use, but he'd never been especially **adept** at reciting Corporation policy. He tried to improve, but no matter what he did, his real personality always colored the words the wrong way and made them sound **asinine**.

"I've got a better idea," she said. "Why don't you leave my mind alone and just tell my parents you 'fixed' me? I promise I'll be good from now on." She batted her eyelashes.

Jaden glanced around the room suspiciously, then took a chance and blurted out, almost under his breath, "Wait a minute, bro. When you came to me three weeks ago, all you wanted was to be cured of your addiction. You saw it as a **liability**. *Which it is*. What's your problem now?"

"*I* am. The world is. I *need*—" Ally twirled in a circle, her arms outstretched, her **azure** miniskirt whipping up "—my music."

Jaden summoned all the **forbearance** he could **muster**. He'd never heard music himself, of course, but all addicts tended to beg to keep their vices when they were **coerced** into a splitting session. He knew he should be **inured** to the **supplication** and **rationalization** by now, but it still **tried** his patience.

"You know you can't go on like this, bro," Jaden said, pushing his dreads out of his eyes. "If you could, you, like, wouldn't be here."

"I've just got to get better at not getting caught," she said.

"Well, you'd better be flippin' outstanding at not getting caught," Jaden said, "'cause the next time you are, they're going to pink-slip you for sure. Trust me, bro—you don't want to end up in the Unemployed Zone."

Ally shuddered and wrapped her arms around her waist. "Fine," she said, **capitulating**. "Let's just get this over with."

Jaden nodded as he took off his braided poncho and slung it on the back of the chair. Addicts tended to come around when he

ingenuous: sincere, straightforward	**forbearance:** leniency or indulgence	**supplication:** begging
adept: skillful	**muster:** gather or summon	**rationalization:** providing untrue reasons for behavior
asinine: inexcusably stupid	**coerced:** forced	**tried:** tests or strains
liability: a disadvantage	**inured:** accustomed to something unpleasant	**capitulating:** giving in
azure: blue like a clear sky		

talked about the Unemployed Zone. Okay, so he didn't know first-hand how bad the Unemployed Zone was, but he'd read the corporate briefing. Once he'd even been to Fort Miami, the gateway to the U.Z. Beyond that well-fortified barrier, civilization ended and addiction began.

As he skimmed his fingertips across the wall console again, the splitting chair in the corner whirred to life, its low rumble almost a purr.

Ally sat in the chair. Jaden strapped her in, and with a few more swipes at the console, the chair adjusted to fit Ally's body. The three-pronged splitter **probe ascended** from the chair to rest along the back of her neck.

"This won't hurt," Jaden said, touching a button on the console. "You may feel a slight . . . *pressure*." A long thin needle slid out of the device and **embedded** itself into her spinal column.

Ally's mind burst into colors and shapes in front of him, a visual representation of what was going on inside of her head. Jaden was a **synesthete**, and his senses got all mixed up from time to time, but he could sense things others couldn't. When he received his first cybernetic implants at thirteen, he could jack into other people's minds and see their personalities as shapes and flashes of color. When he was jacked in, he could see people's addictions as if they had a solid mass. He could even manipulate these shapes and split off the bad parts of an addict's personality. This was the essence of his work as a splitter. He was a drug dealer who had been turned into a drug counselor.

Ally didn't know it, but in Jaden's eyes her inner world swirled neon green, awash with pink and gold spheres and cubes. He guided his mind through the images, through her mind, until he found the place where he had constructed a wall around her vice the last time. Instead of the thick brick wall, he found her music addiction, which glowed an **iridescent** blue. Only a few crumbled bricks remained at

---

probe: testing device
ascended: rose up
embedded: surrounded closely

synesthete: one who hears shapes, sees colors, tastes sounds, etc. (invented word)

iridescent: lustrous or rainbowlike

the bottom. But something didn't seem right. The wall hadn't crumbled; it was as if it had exploded from within. He'd heard about vice walls built by **incompetent** splitters occasionally springing leaks, but this was no leak. The entire wall had been **annihilated**.

He'd have to **ponder** the whys and wherefores of this problem later. The task at hand was to **reconstruct** the wall. Jaden moved his arms around through the air as if conducting, and in a sense, he was. He was guiding the shapes and sounds of Ally's mind through the paths he desired. It was tricky work, but after about half an hour's effort, Ally was good as new. Better, even. She'd no longer have the distraction of an all-consuming addiction to mess up her life. She could return to her upscale house and **elite** high school and prepare for her own unique role within The Corporation. Jaden rolled his eyes at the thought of it.

Jaden slid the **implement** back out of her neck. "You're all set."

Ally blinked.

Jaden undid the straps and stepped back. Sometimes it took them a minute to adjust.

Phlegmatic, Ally rose from her chair with measured, **precise** movements.

Jaden breathed a sigh of relief. She'd be a different girl now. Now that she would no longer chew up the scenery, she'd be able to be a focused, productive employee. No longer would she be diverted from whatever vital role The Corporation, in all its wisdom, might choose for her.

"Let's go show your parents what a **dutiful** employee you've become," he said.

"Yes, Splitter Emory."

Jaden led a **prosaic** Ally down the hall toward the waiting room. She was definitely more manageable, but part of him almost missed her frenetic perkiness. Addicts generally seemed quieter after splitting—**docile** even. He assumed it was a temporary side effect of the

---

incompetent: unqualified
annihilated: completely destroyed
ponder: consider carefully
reconstruct: rebuild

elite: powerful and influential
implement: put to use
phlegmatic: unemotional
precise: exact

dutiful: behaving respectfully
prosaic: dull, unimaginative
docile: obedient

treatment. Nobody complained.

All in all, Jaden was happy about helping Ally, but something still gnawed at him. He'd been proud when he **expurgated** her vice the last time, but it hadn't stuck. What had **induced** his substandard performance? And what guarantee did he have that her addiction would stay walled away this time?

*   *   *   *   *

The Tamlando Detention Center swarmed with addicts and enforcement officers. Amid the **bustle**, Jaden spotted his **fastidious** team leader, Kim Li, talking to Ally's parents. Jaden sometimes wondered what Kim, an **imperious** woman he'd never seen without thick lipstick and even thicker eye shadow, would look like without all that frightening makeup. Even though she was a good six or seven years older than he was, she had a certain **pulchritude**. Her legs had *serious* pulchritude. Or something like that.

Suddenly he became **cognizant** that his hat was still in his jeans pocket. Without it, even the dreads couldn't completely **obscure** the kidney-shaped chrome plate that arched from his temple to the base of his skull. The metal implant might as well be a "Prowling Splitter" sign. Well, too late to do anything about it now. He'd just have to deposit Ally with her parents and bolt before anyone recognized him.

When Kim saw Jaden, she flashed him a grin. Her teeth were perfectly straight and blindingly white. "Jaden! What quick work. I was just telling the Fayres how lucky they were to have such an **adept** splitter assigned to their daughter."

Kim slipped her arm through his. Jaden shifted uncomfortably. It wasn't the **aggrandizement** he minded; it was Kim's familiarity. He wasn't a clingy kind of person, and her intimacy sort of gave him the creeps, as hot as she was. This was his *boss*, after all.

expurgated: cleansed	**imperious:** commanding or	**obscure:** hide
induced: caused to happen	bossy	**adept:** skilled
bustle: noisy activity	**pulchritude:** beauty	**aggrandizement:** high
fastidious: careful	**cognizant:** aware	praise

"He's one of the best in the business. Just got approval to apply to the Ripper Squad, even," she boasted.

Ally stood meekly next to her father.

"She does seem a bit more **sedate**," Mr. Fayre agreed, eyeing his **taciturn** daughter.

Kim continued with even more **luminous endorsements**, but Jaden tuned them out, too busy scanning the hallway. He'd put his old life behind him, and he didn't need any reminders sneaking up on him.

"Uh, I really should be go—."

A hand clasped his shoulder from behind. "*Amsterdam*? Amster-dam-Ass Jaden? Well roll me in nuts and call me a frozen banana. It really *is* you!"

---

sedate: steady and serious   **luminous:** glowing   **endorsements:** expressions
taciturn: silent   of support

Jaden paled. Nobody had called him by his street **alias** in five years.

A **diminutive**, balding man had his hand in Jaden's. He shook it too long, and Jaden just wished the pervy **interposer** would give it back to him.

Ally's parents looked on with **disdain**. Only four kinds of people came to the Detention Center—addicts, enforcement officers, splitters, and dealers. The man's oversize, wrinkled tuxedo and the grubby maroon derby he clutched clearly identified him as an addiction dealer.

"Uh, whoa. Look, bro, maybe I could roll you in nuts some other time, but right now. . . ." Jaden's tone plainly implied that the man was a lunatic. Jaden **scrutinized** the man's narrow, thin face. He tried to place the heavy eyelids and pasty complexion. He'd known a lot of people back in the old days, but he'd put that part of his life away when he became a splitter.

"You clean up better than a pig in a rainstorm!" the dealer continued, patting and pawing Jaden **amicably**.

Kim frowned. "You'd better check your pockets before you let this guy go, Jaden."

Ally's mother **tittered** in response, but an **apathetic** Ally looked on with only mild interest. She hadn't said a single word since she'd been reunited with her parents.

"Uh, I think you've got me mixed up with someone else," Jaden said, **extricating** himself from the man. "I've never even been to Amsterdam." He couldn't really deny that his name was Jaden, obviously. Maybe no one had noticed. Amsterdam had been the nickname the other dealers had given him—a **hackneyed** reference

---

alias: additional name
diminutive: tiny
interposer: someone placed between
disdain: contempt

scrutinized: examined carefully
amicably: in a friendly way
tittered: giggled

apathetic: indifferent
extricating: disentangling
hackneyed: trite or commonplace

to the notoriously permissive laws of a certain city in the European Union.

Jaden just wished the man would leave. **Reputable** splitters didn't have addiction dealers as **acquaintances**.

The man flashed a slick, sideways grin that revealed a gold **incisor**. "Left the streets like a meatball rolling uphill, have we, Amsterdam?"

Jaden regarded the man with a bemused stare, but inside his heart was pounding. He recognized this guy. He hadn't thought of Squeeze at first because Squeeze had been pink-slipped just before Jaden became a splitter. There was no way he'd have been released from the Unemployed Zone already. Yet there he was, standing there with his crooked gold grin.

He had to get out of there, and fast. Squeeze's **vociferous** tone was likely to draw the attention of people he wished to forget even more than Squeeze. Jaden assumed his professional splitter **persona**.

"I'm afraid you'd know more about the streets than I would," Jaden said. "Uh, being *of* the streets yourself."

Kim snickered at Jaden's **implicit denigration** of the addiction dealer.

Jaden turned his back on Squeeze and whipped out a business card for Ally's parents. "So, I really must be going. Please call the Splitter Center if you have any further questions." With a **deft** movement, he stuck his hat back atop his dreads and **loped** down the hall toward the nearest exit.

"Too damn close," he **grumbled** as he pushed out into the mid-morning sunlight.

*   *   *   *   *

reputable: respectable	**persona:** personality shown in public	**deft:** skillful
acquaintances: people one knows	**implicit:** implied or potential	**loped:** moved with an easy gait
incisor: sharp front tooth	**denigration:** intense criticism	**grumbled:** muttered angrily
vociferous: loud		

When Jaden returned to the Splitter Complex, his footsteps echoed in the **commodious** quarters. The half-dozen other splitters he lived with were seeing patients in their offices on the lower floors of the tower. Baqer, the tech, the closest thing Jaden had to a friend at the center, was probably down in the lab with the other tech guys. And of course Jaden had beaten Kim home.

Jaden found it slightly unsettling to find his home empty and quiet. The rooms usually **thrummed** with activity. The Corporation ensured that no one had unproductive time on their hands. He shouldn't be there. He'd head directly down to the offices—as soon as he grabbed something to eat.

As he browsed the pantry for something to **sate** his appetite, Jaden's arm hairs prickled. Someone was watching him.

"You missed the auditors."

Jaden turned to see his **rival**, Reth, leaning against the door frame. A muscular sixth-generation splitter from an **affluent** family, Reth was his nearest **competitor** in the race for the Ripper Squad position. Whereas Jaden wore his hair long in order to partially cover his splitter interface, Reth shaved his head to make his more pronounced.

"Uh, right, dude. Are they coming back?" Jaden asked.

"Dunno."

"Uh, you could have called the center. Or told them I was there, or something." Jaden **rued** the words before they were out of his mouth. He certainly hoped the auditor didn't see him with his first repeat client in five years. Not a **propitious** way to start out a job interview.

"Who says I didn't?" Reth said, smirking as he ran his hand over the stubble on his head.

Jaden rolled his eyes. He couldn't help it: Reth's **spurious** insinuation **irked** him. Reth was lucky that Jaden had put aside his dark past. The thirteen-year-old Jaden Emory would have been pounding the jerk by now.

---

commodious: comfortably spacious
thrummed: hummed monotonously
sate: indulge or satisfy
rival: opponent

affluent: wealthy
competitor: someone striving for the same objective
rued: regretted

propitious: favorable
spurious: false
irked: annoyed

What the hell—the eighteen-year-old Jaden might start pounding him anyway.

Jaden struggled to keep his voice **brusque**. "Dude, you're so **sophomoric**. If you had sent the auditors to T.D.C., I would have seen them."

"Sound a little **flustered** there, Emory. Something not go right at T.D.C.?"

"What—do you know something about it, bro?"

"I do now," Reth said, clearly pleased his little **subterfuge** had gotten Jaden to admit something was wrong.

Jaden turned and dug into the pantry shelves for a snack. "Don't you need to go shave your legs or something, Reth?"

"You wouldn't be this **peevish** if you hadn't screwed something up at T.D.C. Great timing, Emory. You were able to show your best face to the auditors."

"You didn't **dispatch** them to T.D.C. and you know it, so shut your piehole." He grabbed the nearest object, a bag of potato chips, and threw it at Reth, who caught it effortlessly with one hand.

They both heard the front door slide open and high heels click across the **foyer** toward the kitchen. It could only be Kim.

Reth **seized** the bag of chips and popped them open with a single motion. Chips flew all over, and he let the bag fall to his feet just as Kim stormed into the kitchen.

"What the blast is this mess about?" Kim **railed**, gesturing widely at the chips **dispersed** across the tile.

Jaden rolled his eyes. He hated it when Kim used that expression.

"He threw them at me," Reth said, "and the bag popped open."

"Yeah, right." Jaden remarked dryly. "As if I'd risk giving that bald head of yours a chip-induced trauma."

Kim sighed. "So you admit you threw them at Reth. What am I, a daycare manager? Is the child-to-adult ratio too high here, or something? Clean this blast up—no, in my office first."

---

brusque: blunt or harsh
sophomoric: immature and overconfident
flustered: upset
subterfuge: deception

peevish: ill-tempered
dispatch: send
foyer: entrance hallway

seized: took by force
railed: complained angrily
dispersed: scattered

Jaden sighed in disbelief. He was going to get in trouble because of this **dissembler**?

"In my office, Jaden—now," Kim said, turning.

"Don't forget to take your hair with you," piped Reth.

"Now, Jaden," Kim asserted.

dissembler: liar

Jaden had no choice but to **acquiesce**. He followed Kim, with Reth's smirk searing into the back of his neck. Well, Reth could pop all the bags of chips he wanted. How bad could Jaden get busted for making a little mess? Once inside Kim's office, he might even get a chance to **elucidate** what really happened. Not that it mattered that much.

In Kim's office, Jaden flopped into the round chair in front of Kim's desk. He regarded Kim from underneath his blond dreads. "It's not fair, Mom." Jaden joked. "Reth's always **instigating** stuff like this."

"I'm not upset with you because of your **altercation** with Reth—though I am pretty disappointed. You always let him **goad** you. You're better than that, Jaden."

"I admit that guy gets under my skin. I can't help it, Kim."

"You'd better start learning to control yourself if you want to be on the Ripper Squad. They won't **abide** outbursts like yours. Not at all."

"And Reth? He's—"

"We're not talking about Reth here, Jaden. We're talking about you. As your team leader, it's my job to make sure you stay above-board and that you achieve your maximum potential. It hasn't been easy for me, as you well know. . . . "

Jaden rolled his eyes. "How many times am I going to have to be **upbraided** about my past before The Corporation starts trusting me, Kim?"

"When are you going to cease your **ignominious** behavior? When are you going to show yourself as trustworthy, Jaden?"

---

acquiesce: give in   **altercation:** noisy argument   **upbraided:** scolded harshly
elucidate: make clear   **goad:** urge into action   **ignominious:** dishonorable
instigating: provoking   **abide:** tolerate   or humiliating

Kim crossed her legs and pulled her skirt down with a slight squirm. Jaden couldn't help but glance down at her **sinuous** figure.

He swallowed. "When have I ever shown myself *not* to be trustworthy?"

"Try less than an hour ago when you were **impertinent** to those Senior Management clients."

"The girl wasn't Senior Management, just her parents."

"And that's who you were **insolent** to—"

"Ally was my client, not her parents."

"Who do you think paid the bill? The little raver or her Senior Management parents? This is exactly what I'm talking about. I worry about you, Jaden. I've tried to **nurture** you, but sometimes I think you identify with the street element, because of your past—"

Jaden shifted in his seat. "Kim, I'm eighteen now. I'm not the same little kid The Corporation rescued from the streets—"

"The little drug dealer kid, you mean. You were headed straight for the Unemployed Zone. If The Corporation had remained adamant and hadn't taken pity on you, you would have never seen your fourteenth birthday—"

"For which I'm thankful, and I have been for five years, but how much longer do I have to keep **groveling** to **vindicate** myself with The Corporation? I'm a dutiful employee. I'm an **acclaimed** splitter, one of the best, and you know it, or else you never would have recommended me for the Ripper Squad."

"A decision I hope you won't force me to regret."

Jaden looked at her. "Kim, you know you don't mean that."

"I don't know anymore, Jaden. You've been in my charge for so long . . . I wonder if it's colored my **perception**. This next week is so important for you, and for us. You've got to be at the **pinnacle** of your game at all times. The auditors could be **lurking** anywhere, **assessing** your performance to determine whether or not you're fit for the Ripper Squad."

---

sinuous: moving gracefully
impertinent: disrespectful
insolent: bold or insulting
nurture: nourish or educate

groveling: crawling or wallowing
vindicate: free from blame
acclaimed: praised
perception: observation or impression

pinnacle: highest peak
lurking: following or lying in wait
assessing: judging

"Reth said they were here this morning."

"And what if they had been at the T.D.C.? How do you think your **furtive** secret-agent entrance and **boorish** customer service skills would have been rated?"

Jaden didn't really have an answer to that one. He had already played the **scenario** in his own mind and didn't like the outcome.

Kim stood up and walked around her desk. She sat on the edge, giving Jaden another view of her well-toned legs. "You know I only want you to succeed."

"I know," Jaden said, though he didn't entirely **fathom** how Kim's **idiosyncratic** management style helped him succeed.

"I'm not the only one who thinks it's **imperative** that you do well in the next week. Your application to the Ripper Squad has caught the attention of Tamlando Management."

Jaden wrinkled his brow. "Really?"

Kim nodded **sagely**. "Quite definitely. So you see, now, more than ever, it's not just your own future you're competing for. You're representing all of Tamlando. Your achievements will be a matter of pride for all of our division."

No pressure or anything.

"Don't worry, Kim. I won't let The Corporation down," Jaden said.

"Do I detect a note of sarcasm, Jaden? You know perfectly well I've been busting my ass to get you promoted."

Uh-oh. Kim was starting to feel sorry for herself, which meant that Jaden was skating on thin ice.

"Sorry, Kim. I know you've done a lot."

"Not enough, evidently, or we wouldn't be having this conversation."

"No, really. You've been great all these years, helping me, guiding me. I've appreciated it all, every minute of it."

"I can't help but feel that I could have done more." She sniffed

---

furtive: sly or secretive
boorish: rude and insensitive
scenario: sequence of events

fathom: understand
idiosyncratic: individual or peculiar

imperative: absolutely necessary
sagely: wisely

and turned back to her desk. "But there's still time to help you, Jaden. I'll just make you my top project from now on. You know, keep a closer eye on you so I don't repeat the same mistakes of the past myself," she said **officiously**.

"Uh, Kim, I don't think—"

"You've got patients waiting for you, Jaden. You're dismissed," she said **curtly**. As Jaden left Kim's office, he spotted Reth **sauntering** in the other direction. He'd probably been listening the entire time. Jaden shot him a **withering** look from under his dreads and **trudged** toward the Splitter Center.

The Splitter Center was on the lower floors of the **behemoth** Splitter Complex. The dorms took up the top floors, and the labs and practice areas occupied the middle floors. Jaden felt his **indignation** and **discomfiture wane** as he **lumbered** through the familiar space. It gave him the feeling that he knew exactly what to expect, what his day would bring him.

Then Mario surfaced at the center.

"*Hola*, Splitter Emory," Mario said, his broad grin failing to conceal his nervous edginess. Mario's round face always seemed locked open, eyebrows up, eyes wide, with every tooth showing.

Jaden forced himself to sound casual as he shook Mario's hand and greeted him. "What are you doing here, Mario? You're all paid up."

"It's back, man. The thirst. It was gone for a while after you worked on me, but now it's *back*."

Jaden's heart jumped. *Another* failed treatment? What was going on here?

"Of course, Mario. Have a seat." Jaden desperately wanted to **interrogate** the alcoholic teen, but again, his fear of being listened to **deterred** him.

As Jaden prepared, his mind raced with the possibilities. After Mario's first treatment a week ago, Jaden was certain that even the

---

officiously: meddlesomely
curtly: rudely and abruptly
sauntering: strolling
withering: making speechless

trudged: marched tiredly
behemoth: something huge or powerful
indignation: anger at injustice
discomfiture: confusion or embarrassment

wane: dwindle
lumbered: moved heavily
interrogate: question systematically
deterred: prevented

suggestion of alcohol would make the teen shudder with **revulsion**. What could have happened? Had he made a mistake in treatment? This was definitely not the time to be losing his touch.

Jaden jacked into Mario's mind, which swirled in **dynamic** earth colors—browns and rusts, mostly. Mario's alcohol addiction was a **jaundiced** yellow that Jaden had walled away not more than a week ago. Now it seared into Mario's brain like the heat of a solar flare.

Jaden rebuilt the wall, trying not to get distracted by its absence. Perhaps his own lack of focus had caused the teen's wall to weaken and then explode the first time. He withdrew from Mario and **disengaged** the probe.

Mario sat up **docilely**.

"Hold up a sec, Mario. Stay put. I'd like to connect once more."

"Is something wrong?"

"Not at all, bro. Standard quality-control procedures. We want our patients to be one-hundred-percent satisfied with our service."

Mario eased into the chair.

Jaden jacked back in and found the wall around Mario's addiction **intact**. He had half-expected to see a virus of some sort **adhering** to the wall, oozing **corrosive** acid onto the bricks. But he saw nothing so **melodramatic**.

"You're all set, Mario."

"Thanks, Splitter Emory. Maybe next time I see you at The Verve, not here, eh?"

Jaden flashed a forced smile in response. He didn't want the subject of his **inefficacious** treatment to resurface when The Corporation might be listening. Mario left with an **exuberant** wave.

With a half-hour **hiatus** before his next session, Jaden decided to drop in on his friend Baqer to see if he could check his cybernetic implants for him—help him get a handle on these sudden problems he seemed to be having with his patients' addictions **recurring**. He found Baqer, as always, in the lab.

---

revulsion: disgust
dynamic: vital
jaundiced: discolored yellow (by disease)
disengaged: withdrew
docilely: obediently

intact: left whole
adhering: sticking
corrosive: causing destruction through chemical action
melodramatic: overly dramatic

inefficacious: ineffective
exuberant: joyous and enthusiastic
hiatus: break
recurring: occurring again

Baqer was only twenty years old, but way too intelligent to be simply the maintenance man for a bunch of egotistical splitters; Jaden was sure he was headed for bigger and better things someday soon. When Jaden first arrived at the Splitter Complex, he practically **revered** the older and more **sagacious** technician. Now that he had come into his own, they were more like **peers**, and Jaden considered Baqer his friend, probably his best friend.

Jaden found Baqer bent over a **convoluted** mass of metal and wires spread along a white lab table. The other stations in the lab usually buzzed with the repairs and experiments of the other technicians but today it was **atypically** empty.

"Hey, Baqer. Got a second?"

Baqer looked up and beamed. "For you, my friend, anytime."

"I've got maybe half an hour before my next session. Think you might check the **calibration** on my cybernetic implants?"

"You are experiencing a **malfunction**, maybe?"

Jaden stiffened. "Whoa, bro. Who said anything about a malfunction? I just want a checkup." He had tried to sound playful, but regretted the **umbrage** that had crept into his tone.

"Hey, take it easy, my friend. What has happened to my happy-go-lucky Jaden?"

"I know, I know, bro. Sorry for the **snit**. This Ripper Squad stuff has me a bit on edge. I've got to get myself in top operating condition in case an auditor shows up. Reth said they were hanging around today when I was at T.D.C."

Baqer nodded. "Scary-looking types, too. Twins."

"Really? Clones?"

"I know not, my friend, but talk about **stolid**."

Jaden shuddered. Ever since he was a kid, his eerily enhanced perceptions had allowed him to see right through most people. The possibility of meeting two unfathomable auditors chilled him.

Baqer picked up a diagnostic scanner. "Sit, my friend," he said,

revered: honored	**atypically:** unusually	**umbrage:** suspicion or
sagacious: wise	**calibration:** adjustment	resentment
peers: equals	**malfunction:** failure to work	**snit:** tantrum
convoluted: complicated	normally	**stolid:** unemotional

gesturing to a stool. Jaden obeyed and Baqer ran the scanner over the chrome plate above his right temple.

"You would be wise to reconsider your choice of hairstyle, Jaden," said Baqer, brushing away Jaden's dreads from the implant. "You may have noticed that your **cohorts** tend to shave."

"I like my hair," Jaden said.

"Your implant does not. A strand or two of that nasty stuff gets stuck in the jack and your entire **apparatus** could short-circuit."

"Right, and how many times have you actually seen that happen, bro?"

"It's possible."

Jaden laughed. "What's wrong with taking a little risk now and then, Baq? Live a little."

"I believe in science, my friend," Baqer replied. "Science is predictable. A certain behavior begets a certain response. If you want to be calling me risk-averse, I suppose I am," he said **blithely**, always happy to talk about his deepest passion. "This won't hurt," he added as he inserted the diagnostic probe into one of the jacks in Jaden's shiny metal plate. "You may feel a slight . . . *pressure*."

"AAAAH!" Pain seared through Jaden's skull, then abruptly stopped. "Where the hell did you learn that, Baq—the Republican Guard?"

"Your reference is **anachronistic**, my friend," Baqer said, humming to himself as he manipulated his controls.

Jaden cracked a sly smile through his dreads. "Are you sure you don't mean *anaqronistic*, Baqer?"

"Please to be shutting up now, my friend. We have another adjustment to make. With this next bit you may feel a slight pinch, not unsimilar to the bite of a mosquito."

"The word is *dissimilar*, you moron, and mosquitos don't— AAAAAH!" Another flash of pain, which disappeared as abruptly as it had come.

---

cohorts: companions or colleagues
apparatus: instrument or appliance

blithely: lightheartedly

anachronistic: from the wrong time period

When Jaden had been caught at thirteen dealing the latest designer drug, the thought of cybernetic implants had terrified him. But The Corporation had given him an **ultimatum**—receive the implants and become a splitter, or pack for a trip to the Unemployed Zone. He chose the former.

The initial surgery had a recovery time of less than a week, and upgrades now took an hour, with almost **instantaneous** recovery. The cybernetic implants were miraculous. They turned his **innate** talent for reading people into a **viable** career that didn't require him to keep a gun handy. Of course there were times when he missed the more adventurous life he had led as a kid, but The Corporation knew best.

"Very good," Baqer said. "All readings are normal."

Heavy footsteps thudded in the hall. Jaden rolled his eyes in exasperation—he didn't want one of the other splitters finding out that he needed servicing. "So, can we wrap this up, Baq? I've got to get back to my **roster**."

A familiar figure appeared in the doorway: Reth. "Wrap what up?"

Jaden sighed. The bald, overly muscled creep was everywhere. Didn't he have clients of his own? "Just getting a little tune-up," Jaden said.

"So what's wrong with you?"

"Nothing. Just a few hairs getting fried by the implants."

"Gross, Jaden. You should maintain that hardware better."

"Why don't you worry about your own maintenance, Reth? You might do better on tomorrow's exam."

Reth's eyebrows arched. "I see. Trying to get a last-minute upgrade or something? It won't help you. There's only one slot, and it's already been promised to me."

"Yeah, right, bro."

"Ask my dad if you don't believe me. My **heritage** alone is enough

---

ultimatum: final demand
instantaneous: immediate

innate: part of one's essential nature
viable: able to survive or succeed

roster: list
heritage: inheritance or tradition

to make me a shoo-in."

"I don't think it works that way—and I'm not sweating this exam anyhow."

"If it doesn't work that way, how do you think the last five generations of Warrens have become rippers? It's all about **influence**, Emory, about who you know." He smirked. "Too bad you don't know anybody."

"He knows me," Baqer said softly. "And that was enough to get him in for a tune-up the afternoon before the exam."

Reth huffed, then realized the impact of what Baqer was saying. "Well, I know you, too, Baq."

Jaden **stifled** a laugh and Baqer's eyes sparkled mischievously. "It's not just about *who* you know, Splitter Warren. It's about *how* you know them."

"If you're giving Jaden a tune-up, then you have to give one to me too."

"Fine, fine . . . " Baqer said, gesturing toward the stool Jaden had **vacated**. Reth sat down and Baqer hovered the diagnostic scanner over his shaved head.

Baqer turned to Jaden. "I could uncalibrate him for you, for a **meager** fee, of course."

"I'll go get some cash, bro," Jaden said, grinning.

Reth pushed away from the lab table. "I'm not letting you anywhere near me now," Reth said.

With his best mad-scientist look on his face, Baqer limped toward him with the scanner. "Are you sure? Just a little tune-up. It's exactly what you wanted. . . . "

"Stay away from me!" Reth said, stumbling backward and bolting from the lab.

Jaden and Baqer burst into laughter.

*　*　*　*　*

---

influence: have an effect on　vacated: left
stifled: repressed or　meager: scanty or
smothered　insufficient

Jaden's **mirth** after this bit of **retribution** was short-lived. By the end of his **interminable** day, he'd seen a total of four repeat addicts, a whopping half of the eight clients he treated that day.

He knew he should feel better now that he knew nothing was wrong with his equipment, but he couldn't help wishing Baqer had said, "Ah, I see the problem. Here, just a little screw loose." A couple of **expedient** twists and he would have been cured.

But it hadn't been that simple. There was absolutely no mechanical reason for his clients' vices to be resurfacing. That only left one option: Jaden's powers were fading, and on the eve of the **paramount** day of his eighteen years.

He couldn't face the rest of the department that night, especially Reth. Maybe a drive would clear his head. As he ducked down the side **corridor** to the aero-car hanger, Kim flagged him down. Unable to **feign** that he hadn't seen her, he stopped.

"Make sure you're in by bed-check. This second-level Ripper Squad exam tomorrow is going to be **formidable**. It'll be more **arduous** than anything I've ever thrown at you."

"I know. I just need some night air so I sleep well. You can trust me."

"I'd better be able to. Another **bungle** could cost you my recommendation," she said and stalked off.

That woman seriously needs to lighten up, thought Jaden.

Jaden proceeded onward to the top of the center, where all of the flying cars were parked.

Flying cars. Of all the cheesy things Jaden hated about the year 2157, flying cars were the worst. If he had lived a century or so earlier, he would have driven something cool. A Chrysler 300C would have been his style. But no one drove on the actual roads anymore—except in the Unemployed Zone, of course.

Jaden was still **wallowing** in his **distaste** for contemporary culture when he turned the corner to his new red Phoenix 5000 sports

---

mirth: gladness accompanied by laughter
retribution: revenge
interminable: endless
expedient: practical for achieving a certain result

paramount: supreme
corridor: hallway
feign: pretend
formidable: causing fear or awe

arduous: extremely difficult
bungle: mistake
wallowing: indulging
distaste: dislike

aero-car. He started to roll his eyes at the vehicle, then stopped short, **flabbergasted**.

There, leaning against the driver's side door, **weeping**, was Ally Fayre.

---

flabbergasted:
overwhelmed with surprise
weeping: crying

Blue mascara and eye shadow dripped down Ally's face. Her whole body **trembled** with the force of her heaving frame.

"Um, Ally? What are you doing here?"

"You've got to help me." Her voice **quavered**. "You're my only hope. The treatments aren't working."

"Whoa, hold on, let's not be **hasty**, girl. It's only been a day—not even."

"I can't stay away from the raves. You've got to treat me again. You've got to make me better."

Jaden felt a growing sense of unease at her words, but fought to keep his expression calm. It wouldn't help either of them for Ally to know that her seemingly unstoppable addiction was as much of a threat to his well-being as it was to hers. "Look, I was just going out for a drive. Want to come?" It wasn't safe to talk in the parking garage, and probably not even in his stupid flying car. The Corporation listened everywhere.

Ally nodded, and they rode in silence to the Ybor City Mall.

Jaden knew the mall had sensors, too, but he figured they were probably focused on catching shoplifters or identifying drug dealers, not tracking the conversations of two shopping teenagers. Even if one *was* a raver and the other looked like a dealer.

Once safely inside the mall, Jaden spoke. "How do you know you can't avoid the raves? Your addiction is securely walled away in your mind. I saw to that. All it will take now is a little behavioral modification on your part. Stay away from the friends who took you to the raves. Burn all your **contraband**, including the stuff your parents don't know about. Behave like a productive

---

trembled: shivered
quavered: spoke tremblingly

hasty: fast or impatient

contraband: smuggled goods

Employee of The Corporation, and your cravings will go away in no time."

"I've already been back to a rave. This afternoon."

"How? Didn't your parents—"

"They don't care where I go or what I do as long as they don't have to see me."

"Even after you were arrested?"

"They'd like to forget they have an addict as a daughter." She snorted out a laugh. "Besides, you cured me, remember? The super-adept cybernarc, or however that scary Asian woman described you. What did they have to worry about?"

The balding security guard next to the food court eyed them. "We'd better keep moving," Jaden said, taking her by the elbow. "The walls have ears—not to mention the balding security guards."

"What are you so worried about? This is my problem, not yours," Ally said.

"Bro, you're making this my problem by asking me to treat you again."

"So you'll do it?"

Jaden turned and took her hands in his. "Ally, you're a **neophyte** when it comes to dealing with the system. If I treat you again, I'm supposed to pink-slip you as an **incorrigible**. You know where a pink slip gets you, right?"

Ally paled. "But I'm asking for treatment, not prison. I want to get better. I really do."

"They don't factor in intent here. Three strikes and you're out. You'll be **remanded** to the Unemployed Zone."

Ally gasped. "There has to be some **alternative**."

"There isn't," Jaden said, knowing full well that he actually had some **discretion** in the matter. It didn't matter, though. He couldn't have Ally coming back to the center to be retreated, not with those auditors hanging around the center. The Corporation

---

neophyte: beginner
incorrigible: depraved or unmanageable

remanded: ordered back
alternative: another choice

discretion: individual choice

would discover his powers were on the fritz, and he'd never get promoted to the Ripper Squad.

"Then you might as well turn me in now. I'll end up there eventually. One day they'll arrest me at another rave, and I'll finally be out of my parents' hair for good. They'll have to deal with the **humiliation** of having a worthless addict like me as a daughter, but—"

"Cut it out already! If you really want to quit, why don't you just do it? Grow a backbone, get some guts. It's all about **fortitude**."

"I can't, I just can't. You make it sound so easy, but you have no idea what I'm going through." Ally buried her face in her hands.

"I've treated thousands of addicts over the last five years, and they all have some sob story—whether they're addicted to video games, alcohol, or music." Filled with **derision**, Jaden's voice **mocked** hers. "'It's so hard. I can't do it on my own. You've got to help me!'" Jaden pulled Ally's hands from her face. "Get over yourself, Ally."

"You're such a hypocrite, Jaden. You slouch around with these big dreads, acting all cool, you obviously have a past, and yet you stand there lecturing me like the big, **supercilious** *narc* you are."

Jaden was speechless.

"Look, I don't need this. You're not better than me. If you won't help me, I'll find someone who will. You're not the only splitter in Tamlando, you know. I hear Reth Warren is also quite **proficient**. Some might say better."

"Look, any splitter you go to will have to pink-slip you. The computers are linked. They'll know this is your third time for treatment."

"My parents won't let me end up in the Unemployed Zone."

"If that's the case, why are you sneaking around behind their backs, demanding treatment on the sly?" Jaden asked. "Because they're so supportive of you and your addiction?"

Ally folded her arms across her chest. "Take me home."

"No problem." He'd be glad to be rid of her.

---

humiliation: destruction of self-respect or dignity
fortitude: strength of mind

derision: ridicule or scorn
mocked: made fun of or imitated

supercilious: condescending
proficient: skillful or expert

As they neared Ally's home, she finally spoke. "Cut the lights. It's past my curfew."

Jaden shut off the headlamps. This girl was bound to get him in trouble one way or another. His stupid Phoenix 5000 slid onto the darkened landing pad next to Ally's parents' home in the **estimable** upper-class neighborhood.

Ally paused, her finger hovering above the button to open the door. She turned to Jaden, her upturned face filled with fear and desperation. "Are you sure there isn't anything you can do for me? Some alternate path I don't know about? It doesn't matter how hard it is. I'll do whatever it takes. . . . " Her voice faded off painfully.

Jaden started to answer her, but realized he hadn't the slightest clue what to say. Corporate Culture didn't leave that many options for dealing with addiction.

A blinding **shaft** of light pierced the night. A dark figure was **silhouetted** in the doorway.

"What are you doing with my daughter?" a deep voice boomed.

As Ally **cowered**, Jaden searched for an excuse. "Umm . . . well . . . ummm . . . good evening, sir!" came his **inarticulate** stammer.

Mr. Fayre glared at the pair without saying another word.

Ally bounced to life. "Hi, Daddy!" she called, as if nothing on earth was wrong. She bounded out of the car and around to Jaden's side. She opened the door and pulled Jaden toward her father.

"You remember Splitter Emory, don't you, Daddy? We met at the Ybor Mall. I was out spending my allowance like a good employee. Jaden complimented me on how well I was doing and offered me a ride home. Isn't that right, Jaden?"

Mr. Fayre ignored Ally's **blathering**. "You're late. It's past your curfew."

"Not much, Daddy, and I would have been even later if it wasn't for Jaden. I just lost track of the time at the mall, that's all."

"What a **feeble alibi**. If you spent all your allowance, where are

---

estimable: worthy of high regard
shaft: beam shining through an opening
silhouetted: outlined against a lighter background

cowered: shrank away in fear
inarticulate: unclear, at a loss for words
blathering: talking foolishly

feeble: weak
alibi: excuse

the shopping bags?"

"It's all being delivered. I didn't think I'd have a ride home until I met Jaden."

"You can **fabricate** whatever stories you'd like, but I know the truth. You probably spent it all at some *rave*."

"Daddy, I'm cured. Ask Jaden. I don't do that stuff anymore."

"It doesn't matter if you're still raving or not. You'll always be an addict—and an embarrassment."

Jaden heard his own life echoed in Ally's. Just as Ally's father would always see her as an addict, Jaden feared The Corporation would always see him as the kid dealer they had scraped up off the streets so many years ago. But he'd gone through a **metamorphosis**, and so could Ally. They might not see it yet, but they would.

He couldn't allow Mr. Fayre to **abase** his daughter further. "In my professional opinion, she's doing quite well."

Mr. Fayre narrowed his eyes. "In your *professional* opinion? What profession would that be—professional skateboarder? Besides, it's only been a day."

"Recidivism is almost **nonexistent** in my line of work."

"And is that why you had to treat her twice?"

"A small leak in the **fortifications**, that's all. Firmly patched and well secured, I assure you. You've got a good girl here, Mr. Fayre, and more important, an outstanding employee for The Corporation."

Mr. Fayre snorted. "That'll be the day."

"Daddy, it's true—"

"Don't you 'Daddy' me! Get inside, Ally. Now."

Ally glanced **circumspectly** at Jaden and **plodded** inside, leaving Jaden facing Mr. Fayre alone.

Mr. Fayre's voice remained firm, but it lost its **incensed** edge. "Look, despite the freaky hair, you look like a well-intentioned kid, Jaden. Leave my daughter alone, for your own sake. She's nothing

---

fabricate: invent or construct
metamorphosis: transformation
abase: lower in respect

nonexistent: not present in reality
fortifications: walls that strengthen or protect
circumspectly: cautiously

plodded: walked heavily or slowly
incensed: angry

but trouble." He **extinguished** the porch light and went inside.

Jaden wanted to follow him, to **decry** his hateful words about his daughter, but he **abstained**. He had a better way of making Mr. Fayre understand. Just like The Corporation had helped him all those years ago, he'd help Ally become the person she wanted to be, no matter what the cost. And he knew just how to do it.

* * * * *

Back at the Splitter Center, Jaden found Baqer, as always, in the lab, **tinkering** with a splitting chair. A panel of **effulgent** lights and shiny circuitry **coruscated** on one side.

"Big old piece of machinery," Jaden said.

"Indeed," Baqer answered, his head still buried in his work.

"Too bad it's not smaller. We could do splitting house calls, without all the heavy equipment."

"Indeed, my friend," Baqer said.

"But I bet it's not possible. Too much **infrastructure** to reproduce . . . "

Baqer finally looked up. "That is where you are wrong, my friend. The chair doesn't do much but **immobilize** the patient. You could do that with a drug, or just a good set of restraints wherever you were."

"But placing the probe is a delicate matter—"

"Sure, the chair adjusts, defining the measurements **integral** for placing the probe precisely, but the same thing could be done with a bit of a head **contrivance**. Not as classy as a nice leather chair, but it would do the trick."

"Seems you've already been **cogitating** on something like this," Jaden said.

Baqer grinned. "Tuning up splitters isn't the most challenging job in the world. It affords me ample opportunity to think."

extinguished: put out	**effulgent:** brilliant	**integral:** essential
decry: strongly criticize	**coruscated:** sparkled	**contrivance:** artificial
abstained: kept oneself from doing	**infrastructure:** basic framework	arrangement
tinkering: repairing or experimenting	**immobilize:** prevent from moving	**cogitating:** thinking

"Could you perhaps think me up a house-call version of the splitting equipment, then? Uh, speaking **hypothetically** of course."

"I would love to develop any product Management directs," Baqer replied amiably.

Jaden paused. Could he trust Baqer enough to tell him that the project was his and not Management's? If he told Baqer what he was planning and Baqer didn't **accede**, his plan could be **foiled** before it even started. Baqer would have to turn him in.

He should just dismiss the entire discussion as **speculative**. But Jaden wasn't about to **forsake** Ally, and if he went ahead with the project on his own and someone found out, his conversation with Baqer could point the finger at him.

Forget it—at this point he was doomed either way. He'd just have to trust his friend.

Jaden picked up a pencil and scribbled softly on Baqer's notebook. *What if it wasn't a Management project, bro?*

Jaden knew the **enormity** of what he was implying. Private practice and free enterprise were strictly forbidden by The Corporation. There were no projects other than Management projects.

Baqer opened a drawer and flipped a hidden switch deep inside.

"It's safe to talk now," he said. "I've rigged a bypass around the security and monitoring system. It doesn't last very long, but it turns the lab into a temporary safe room."

"**Ingenious**! How'd you do it?"

"As I told you, my friend, I have far too much time on my hands," Baqer said, his eyes sparkling. "So what on earth have you gotten yourself into?"

Jaden told Baqer about his fading powers, and about Ally and the others who had returned for second treatments.

"I need to figure out what's wrong with me before I mess up more people," Jaden finished.

"And before the auditors find out there's something wrong

---

hypothetically: assuming for the sake of argument
accede: give in
foiled: defeat or frustrate

speculative: theoretical
forsake: abandon

enormity: huge importance
ingenious: clever and original

with you, huh?"

"Well, that, too," Jaden admitted.

"An **efficacious** diagnosis of the problem is definitely needed, and it can't be done here without **disclosing** your problem and theirs."

"So you can see why the portable splitting apparatus is the **linchpin** in this project."

"Of course."

"So how long do you think it might take you to put it together?"

"Not long. A day, maybe. I've actually worked out most of the details already. I was planning on putting something together to show Management—"

"They can't ever know what we've done," Jaden **interjected**. "This **collusion** has got to be our secret alone. Agreed?"

Baqer nodded. "I—"

Suddenly the lights cut off, leaving them in **unmitigated** darkness.

---

efficacious: effective
disclosing: revealing

linchpin: key element
interjected: introduced or interrupted

collusion: secret cooperation
unmitigated: unrelieved

"Curfew!" Jaden hissed. They had talked too long. When The Corporation said "lights out" it meant "lights out." No warning, nothing. The lights just went out. All over the Splitter Center.

And with the power out, odds were that Baqer's security bypass was out as well.

"Tomorrow afternoon," Jaden whispered, hoping Baqer would understand. He could hear Baqer scurrying to hide the notes from their conversation. He desperately wanted Baqer's confirmation that he'd keep their project **clandestine**, but there was no time for that now. If they weren't both in bed by automatic bed-check, they'd be in big trouble.

Jaden scrambled toward the dorms. There wasn't a second to spare.

After five years in the center, Jaden knew his way in the dark and had all the shortcuts memorized. He slid under the covers just as the red line of the bed-scan passed over him.

*   *   *   *   *

The next morning, Jaden awoke before the rest of the department. He had to get a message to Ally, to let her know to **persevere** for just a little longer. The phone wasn't any good—just about any message **transmission** could be bugged. He'd have to rely on the old-fashioned way; he'd have to go talk to her.

Jaden parked his stupid flying car in the garage **adjacent** to Gibson High and then haunted the bus drop-off, waiting for Ally.

---

clandestine: secret   **transmission:** sending   **adjacent:** next to
persevere: keep on

He wore his crocheted cap and poncho—Ally wouldn't be able to miss him.

But Jaden almost missed her. If it hadn't been for her blueberry-colored pigtails, this time bound tastefully without **embellishment** at the base of her neck, Jaden would have never recognized her. The school uniforms all blended together in a sea of black-and-white **monotony**.

Ally almost walked right past him as she chatted with two other girls. Jaden reached out and touched her arm. "Hey, bro."

She snatched her arm away. "Excuse me?" she said, her voice that of the privileged elite. Jaden cocked his head and looked down his nose at her. His heavy dreads fell in his eyes. "Ally, it's *me*, Jaden."

What was he expecting from her, a look of **elation**?

"What are you doing here?" she asked, her voice clipped.

"I wanted to tell you something."

One of the uniformed girls with her snapped her gum. "Do you know this *narc*?" she said nasally. Obviously another good Senior Manager's brat.

"Kind of. Why don't you two go on ahead, and I'll catch you at lunch?" Ally said.

"Whatever," the second girl said, rolling her eyes. The pair tromped off down the hall.

"What do you mean, 'kind of,' Ally? And for your information, I'm a *splitter*, not a narc."

"Same difference. And what are you doing at my school, with your stupid dreads waving all over and your freakish implants out for everyone to see? Do you think I want my friends to see me with a cybernarc?"

"Oh? Is that why you're afraid to be seen with a splitter? Or is it that you're afraid your friends will find out there's something wrong with you, Ally?"

Ally grabbed him by the arm and pulled him away from the **throng**

---

embellishment: decoration   **elation:** joyfulness or pride   **throng:** crowd
monotony: boring repetition

of high schoolers. "My business is my business, you jerk."

"You can't just go around **affecting normalcy**."

"Nice vocabulary, narc. And isn't that what you told me to do? 'Act like a normal person and you *will* be normal.' Hypocrite."

"You can't **disavow** what's been happening to you. You'll end up just like your parents."

"Leave my parents out of this."

"Look, I just came to help you."

In the background, the bell rang.

"I'm going to be late. I've got to go."

"I thought you wanted my help?" Jaden said, thoroughly **flummoxed** by her **obstinate demeanor**.

"I do, just not here. Not now."

"That's what I came to tell you. I've found a way to help you. You'll have to meet me—"

"I can't do this now. I'll get detention if I don't leave—"

"Fine, but the Unemployed Zone is a lot rougher than some high school detention."

"You don't understand. I can't get in trouble again."

"That's what I'm trying to do—keep you out of trouble!"

"Jaden—"

"Forget it!" he yelled. He balled the piece of paper with the address and threw it at her. "Meet me or not. I'm not the one who's going to wind up in the Unemployed Zone performing lewd acts for five dollars just so I can feed my addiction." He turned and stormed off, his dreads flopping wildly around his face.

Jaden **revved** the engine to his stupid Phoenix 5000 flying car. Blast, she made him so mad! All he was trying to do was help her. Why did she have to be so **intractable**?

Did he actually just use the word *blast*?

He was still **irascible** when he returned to the Splitter Center. Why was he bothering to put himself in jeopardy for her anyhow?

---

affecting: pretending
normalcy: state of being normal
disavow: refuse to acknowledge

flummoxed: confused
obstinate: stubborn
demeanor: manner or behavior

revved: operated at high speed
intractable: unmanageable
irascible: easily made angry

He punched his pass card into the reader and the door slid open. He **glowered** at the receptionist as he stalked toward his office. She returned his look with a startled expression.

"Splitter Emory, why aren't you at the exam?"

"Blast!" With Ally on his mind, he'd totally forgotten the second-level splitter exam. Jaden whirled and **bounded** through the halls toward the testing center. So far he was only a couple minutes late. With a bit of luck, he'd be able to slip in back without anyone noticing.

What was he thinking? This wasn't some entry-level job application. There were only two candidates for the job—himself and Reth. Certainly they'd have noticed that fifty percent of the test-takers hadn't shown up. He might even be **disqualified** for his tardiness.

Jaden **peered** in the window at the testing room. Everyone else had already been **convened**. **Restive**, Reth tapped his fingers on either side of the testing monitor, itching to begin. In the front of the class, the two auditors stood with their backs to the door. Kim faced the door, talking **animatedly** to the two women.

Jaden padded down the **aisle** and slid into his seat. The testing monitor blinked an irritating green-and-white "PENDING" logo. No wonder Reth was going stir-crazy.

"Well," Kim said, "It was quite kind of you to answer my questions. I won't delay your exam any longer."

"Certainly," the auditors answered, turning around in **unison**.

The twins were about Kim's age and identical from their straight long brown hair to their navy suits and stiletto heels. They had an **aloof**, faraway look about them, as if the instructions for their actions filtered in from some alternate authority hidden in the heavens.

Creepy.

"Now—" the first auditor said.

---

glowered: stared angrily
bounded: leapt
disqualified: eliminated from a competition
peered: looked curiously

convened: summoned or caused to assemble
restive: fidgety
animatedly: in a lively way

aisle: passage between seats
unison: at the same time
aloof: emotionally distant

"—we begin," the second auditor finished.

Jaden dug into his exam, and although the test was tough, he felt pretty good about his performance. He was a bit more distracted than he'd have liked, but after what he'd been through over the last day, he'd expected no less. No, he had done well, and now it was all up to the auditors to make the decision. He left the testing room a bit **cocky**, whistling to himself.

Outside, Kim waited for him. "It's a good thing you showed up when you did," she said. "I don't think I could have stalled those keyboard-jockeys another minute."

"You were stalling them? What for?"

"For you, stupid. Can't have the test start without one of my top performers in attendance."

"I didn't think you saw me come in."

"You're a bit hard to miss, Jaden." She bumped him playfully on the shoulder.

"Well, thanks, Kim."

"Let's go out to dinner tonight to celebrate," Kim said. "Just the two of us."

"Celebrate what?"

"Your **imminent** ripper-dom, of course."

"That's a bit **premature**, don't you think? Maybe when I actually get the promotion we can **revel**." Jaden hated to put her off, but he had to meet Ally tonight, assuming she showed up, that was.

"It's a date, then," Kim said, giving him a quick peck on his cheek. Her lipstick left a stain that he was still trying to **efface** when he arrived at the lab.

The exam had gotten him the afternoon off, so Jaden and Baqer had plenty of time to work out the details of the portable splitting equipment. After a few hours of work, they had a functioning **prototype**.

Baqer, you're flipping **phenomenal**, you know that?"

---

cocky: boldly self-confident   **revel:** celebrate   **prototype:** original model
imminent: about to happen   **efface:** make vanish   **phenomenal:** extraordinary
premature: too early

"Indeed."

"You're wasting your time as a maintenance man for a bunch of **pretentious** splitters."

"Indeed."

"Baqer."

"Yes?"

"Why isn't there a *u* in your name? You look like someone tried to cheat at Scrabble."

"You can be shutting up, now, my friend."

"Seriously, Baqer—what are you doing here? Why don't you apply for a promotion?"

"Did."

"Did what?"

"Got offered a promotion two years ago."

"So why didn't you take it?"

"My mother was sick."

"And they haven't given you other chances. If the bosses could see how mad your skills are, I bet they'd be **swayed**."

Baqer shook his head. "Been turned down ever since."

"The Corporation sucks," Jaden said softly, glad the security by-pass was on.

"The Corporation never forgives a betrayal," Baqer said, causing a shiver to run down Jaden's spine.

---

pretentious: with exaggerated importance   **swayed:** influenced

By the end of the afternoon, Baqer had accomplished what no other splitter maintenance tech had ever attempted, much less achieved. Jaden left the lab with a small duffle bag full of equipment that would allow him to split Ally and anyone else he'd like, with minimal notice.

That night when Jaden **absconded** with his **laden** duffle bag after dinner, Baqer cornered him in the hall.

"I'm going with you," Baqer said.

"I can't ask you to **implicate** yourself further, dude."

"You'll need help with the equipment."

"You made it so that I didn't need help."

"But it's the first time," Baqer argued.

"You want to see your brain-child work, am I right?"

A **sheepish** grin crept over Baqer's face. "Indeed."

"You'll never get that promotion if you get caught **conspiring** with me. You've already done too much for me."

Baqer's lower lip **protruded**. "I promise I'll take notes for you, okay?" Jaden said.

Baqer brightened. "Come see me when you get back?"

"Promise."

*   *   *   *   *

Jaden's **rendezvous** hideout was an unobtrusive cabana-style house in Old Hyde Park. The neighborhood had once been a haven for pretentious Senior Management types like Ally's parents, but they

---

absconded: left secretly
laden: loaded
implicate: involve

sheepish: embarrassed
conspiring: plotting

protruded: stuck out
rendezvous: meeting

had all since moved to the corridor, preferring the longer commute to the inner-city **strife** of Tamlando. The house had belonged to Baqer's mother. When he stuffed the pass card into Jaden's palm, Baqer mumbled that he hadn't been back since her death, not even to sell the place.

Jaden **discerned** the ghost of Baqer's mother in every corner of the tasteful little **bungalow**. Despite the permission he'd been granted, he felt like an intruder in a home so lovingly **adorned**. Each ceramic penguin and crystal polar bear remained exactly where Baqer's mother had left it two years ago. The layer of dust on everything gave testament to his **somber** surroundings.

Settling on the **parlor** as the best place to work, Jaden opened his duffle bag on the coffee table and assembled the splitting apparatus the way Baqer had taught him. The probe reminded him of a tick, with its oval body and long, barbed legs.

The only part of the process that worried him was the immobilization drug. Baqer had assured him that the effects were only temporary, and that it was required to ensure proper insertion of the probe, but thinking of Ally lying helpless bothered him. What if something went wrong?

Of course, unless Ally showed up, nothing would happen at all. As the minutes ticked away, Jaden became more and more certain she'd bailed. She was probably still mad at him for embarrassing her in front of her friends.

Three hours past their appointed time to meet, Jaden decided to stop **dithering** and pack up. He couldn't **forestall** the inevitable reality. She wasn't delayed; she simply wasn't coming.

Crash!

The noise came from the backyard.

"Dammit!" the intruder muttered.

Silence, then a **cacophonous cadence** of crashes.

Jaden looked out the window to see Ally playing the garbage cans

---

strife: conflict or struggle
discerned: recognized
bungalow: one-story house with low roof
adorned: decorated

somber: dark and gloomy
parlor: room for receiving guests
dithering: acting indecisively

forestall: prevent
cacophonous: harsh-sounding
cadence: rhythm

like a drum set, dancing to her own beat. He raced outside.

"Stop that!" Jaden said, yanking her away from the garbage.

"I'm not finished!" Ally said **querulously**, furrowing her brow.

"Someone will hear!" Jaden hissed, guiding her inside.

"Everyone should hear!" Ally shouted. "Let the music ring!" She waved her hands in the air, conducting an **ethereal** symphony.

She smelled of smoke and sweat. Her hair was back in bobbing blueberry-colored pigtails, this time dusted with glitter that covered the couch as she **flounced** onto it.

"You're late," Jaden said **dourly**.

"Sorry, *dad*," Ally said sarcastically.

"You've just left a rave, haven't you?" Jaden asked.

"The best one yet! The music was just so pounding and **euphoric**, and the technoshaman had us all in the palm of his hand." She leaped from the couch to demonstrate. "First he'd let the music build, all slow and steady, but louder and faster," Ally said, her head down, dancing to the **crescendo** of a remembered beat. "Then he'd take us higher and higher, until we almost crested, the music just *wham bang whiz*!" she cried, flinging her arms upward and waving them like some giant sunflower, head upturned, beaming at an unseen sun.

Jaden grabbed her by the shoulders. "Yo, snap out of it," he said, shaking her. "You're not at the rave anymore."

"Oh," she said, **crestfallen**. "I'm not, am I?" She looked **vapidly** around at her surroundings.

"You're here to get cured, remember."

"Am I sick?"

"Uh, I think you pretty much are, Ally. You're an addict. I wouldn't really describe what you're doing as normal."

"Who made you the expert on normal, Mr. Cyber-hypocrite? What am I addicted to?"

"Music."

---

querulously: in a whiny way **dourly:** harshly or gloomily **crestfallen:** ashamed
ethereal: otherworldly **euphoric:** joyful **vapidly:** dully
flounced: moved jerkily or bouncily **crescendo:** climax

Her head bobbed. "Oh, I do love music."

"We can fix that. I brought some really cool tools with me, and—"

"I don't want to be fixed."

"What, you're no longer interested in **placating** your parents and The Corporation? They want a nice productive employee, not some **negligent** addict."

"To hell with my parents *and* The Corporation! To hell with *you*, cyberposer. Let the music ring!" Ally swirled around again, **gyrating** to her own internal music.

Her behavior was **abstruse** to him. It wasn't just that of someone high on something she was addicted to. Something else was at work here. Music addicts didn't usually act this intensely. Her behavior reminded him of the effects of hard drugs like maze and skate, designer drugs that had been popular back when Jaden was dealing.

"What else did you take, Ally? What are you high on?"

"Life, Jaden! Joy! Music!" She clutched his hands. "Dance with me! Don't you hear the music?"

Her hands were **frigid**, coated with sweat. He pulled his own hands away.

"You've got to control your addiction, Ally, or your **temerity** will get us both busted. I've gone to a lot of effort to get us here, to get you healed, because *you* wanted it—and now you don't want my help?"

"Calm yourself, narc. You're much too intense. You need to let go once in a while. You need to feed the need, you know?"

Jaden collapsed on the couch. "I don't know what you want, Ally. You're so **capricious**. One minute you want to be healed, and then you're sure you don't. Which is it?"

"Music isn't a disease, Jaden," Ally said in a conspiratorial whisper, sitting down beside him and leaning in until her face was inches from his. "It's a liberation."

"You call this liberation? How are you supposed to be a 'produc-

placating: soothing	**abstruse:** difficult to	**temerity:** recklessness
negligent: careless	understand	**capricious:** impulsive
gyrating: spinning around	**frigid:** cold	

tive employee' behaving like this? What the hell's the matter with me that I keep trying to help someone who doesn't want to be helped? All I'm trying to do is help you be the person you said you wanted to be. What's so **egregious** about that?"

With uncharacteristic **sobriety**, Ally looked at him intensely with her bright aqua eyes. "Jaden, I don't want to be cured." Without warning she leapt to her feet. "I want to dance!" She became a one-person **maelstrom** whirling around the living room faster and faster until she barreled into a standing lamp and turned it over. The room crashed into darkness, the only light that of the full moon and the streetlight outside.

At that moment Jaden made a decision. It was for her own good. If he didn't find a way to calm her down, Ally could send herself into cardiac arrest. Besides, incorrigible addicts could be forced into treatment with the right paperwork. He'd just do the same without the proper forms. He'd be doing himself, Ally, and The Corporation a favor. No more **vacillating** on Ally's part.

Jaden filled the syringe with the immobilization drug, the bottle catching a **glimmer** of moonlight. He tapped the needle twice to remove any air bubbles.

His voice deepened when he spoke, the reassuring **mandate** of authority. "Ally, come here."

Ally froze. She tilted her head. "What is it, Jaden?"

"Come here," he repeated. "Now."

Ally came and sat next to him.

His voice was **staid** and **serene**. "I'm going to give you this drug. Then you're going to lie very still while I insert this probe," he said, picking up the tick-shaped splitting device. "Then I'll remove what's bothering you, and you'll finally be free. Do you understand?"

"I'm not going to let you put that in me," Ally said. "I want to keep my music. Blast my parents, blast The Corporation, and blast you!" She got up and stormed toward the back door.

---

egregious: noticeably bad	**vacillating:** wavering	**staid:** serious
sobriety: seriousness	**glimmer:** faint light	**serene:** calm
maelstrom: strong whirlpool	**mandate:** order	

Jaden knew this would be his last chance to help her. If she walked out the door, the next time he'd see her was in the lineup for the Unemployed Zone.

He lurched off the couch and tackled her from behind. They both landed on the dusty carpet with the wind knocked out of them. "This won't hurt, Ally," Jaden panted. "You may feel a slight . . . *pressure*."

"If it feels so good, why don't you stick it up your own—*oof*!" gasped Ally, as Jaden pinned her.

The syringe **glinted** in the moonlight. Ally knocked it out of his hand and it flew just out of his reach.

Ally tried to break loose, but Jaden **subdued** her. He straddled her stomach and held her hands above her head, grinding them into the threadbare rug.

"This is for your own good." He latched both wrists together with one hand and stretched for the syringe with the other. "I'm trying to help you." He caught the syringe with the very tips of his fingers, but it tumbled out of reach again. Jaden rocked and leaned, lessening the pressure on Ally's stomach.

It was just enough. Ally rolled on her side and kneed him in the gut, pushing herself away from him.

Jaden doubled over in pain, watching Ally **flee**. As she opened the door, she took one terrified glance over her shoulder. The **duress**, shock, and horror in her expression jolted Jaden out of his **rage**. What had he done? This wasn't him.

"Ally, wait!" he yelled.

The back door slammed in response.

Jaden limped to his feet. He had to follow her, to find her before the cops did. In her **addled** state, she'd tell them everything. They'd take her in for addiction, and he'd be arrested for **misfeasance**—splitting services outside an authorized facility.

More than any of this, though, he had to apologize to her. What kind of **reprobate** had he become, forcing his treatment on someone like that? He had always seen himself as laid-back, on the side

---

glinted: reflected light brightly
subdued: brought under control

flee: run away
duress: force
rage: extreme anger
addled: confused

misfeasance: action performed improperly
reprobate: evil person

of the addicts rather than the authorities. How had he suddenly become worse than Reth?

A new and troubling thought occurred to him. What he'd just done—wasn't that what rippers did? They forced treatment on imprisoned incorrigibles. Would his new job, if he got it, be any different than the wholesale rape of addicts' minds?

No, that was different. It wasn't a fair comparison. Prisoners who'd committed serious crimes, like murder, deserved to be treated whether they asked for it or not. It was nothing like forcing Ally to have her addiction to music **expunged**.

Jaden gathered his equipment and tried to erase any signs that he and Ally had been there before he rushed out into the night to find her. She could be anywhere, except home. She'd never go home high. So where would she go to feel **inviolable** and protected?

A rave. She had to be heading back to that rave. But raves were **covert** affairs. Only those in the know could find them. And normal employees treated splitters like cops. He couldn't just waltz up to some lowlife and say, "Hey, which way to the **illicit** rave?" It didn't work that way.

Well, he couldn't just stand around and wait for a rave to appear. He had to at least try.

He cruised his stupid flying car through the darkened streets of Tamlando, figuring that since she was on foot and he had the car, he might find her if he drove around the bungalow in ever-widening loops. The **infrequent** streetlamps glowed faintly, leaving **nebulous** circles amid patches of asphalt. After an hour, he hadn't found a single clue. She must have caught a cab and hightailed it. She could be anywhere by now.

He glanced at his watch. Dammit! Twenty minutes until curfew. He had to head home immediately, or he'd miss bed-check.

Then he saw his answer. A short man in a maroon derby **loitered**

---

expunged: destroyed or erased
inviolable: secure
covert: secret

illicit: illegal
infrequent: uncommon or scarce

nebulous: vague or indistinct
loitered: hung around

beneath a neon sign outside a shady restaurant. If anyone could help him find Ally, it was Squeeze. If he was still the same **miscreant** Jaden knew from the old days, there wasn't a single person more tapped into the seedy underbelly of Tamlando than Squeeze.

But was that really what he wanted? Did he want to be associated with the criminal element he'd spent the last five years trying to distance himself from?

Jaden paused, wrestling with the internal dilemma. Well, it wasn't like he was going into business with Squeeze or anything. He just needed him to help him find Ally.

Jaden landed his car next to the dealer and leaned out the window. "Yo, Squeeze!"

Squeeze peered into the car, then seeing who it was, leaned **nonchalantly** against the wall and tilted his derby down over his eyes.

"It's me, *Amsterdam*! What's up, Squeeze?"

"Are *you* addressing *I*?" Squeeze asked with mock **hauteur**, his thick eyelids drooping.

"Okay, dude, I deserved that."

"That—and more."

"Well . . . maybe I should let my money do the talking for me, bro."

Squeeze tipped his derby back on his head revealing his high, creased forehead. "What exactly would you be needing?"

"What makes you think I need something?"

"Because you're offering me money, Nimrod. Besides, it's the way of the streets—everybody needs *something*."

"It's your way, too. You could help me get something, if I needed it."

"You must be mistaken, sir," Squeeze said, his **dismissive** tone **emulating** Jaden's in the Detention Center.

"Stop busting my chops, Squeeze. I said I was sorry."

"When?"

"Well, I'm saying it now. I need your help, Squeeze. I need to

---

miscreant: criminal or vicious person
nonchalantly: casually

hauteur: arrogance
dismissive: not taking seriously

emulating: imitating

find a girl—"

"A fine young boy like you should be drawing them like marsh-mallows to gators," Squeeze said, his gold-toothed grin curling up as he gave Jaden a **leer**. "Or are your dreads not working for you like they used to?"

"A particular girl. She was with me at the Detention Center. Her name is Ally Fayre."

"What makes you think I'd know where this **trollop** of yours might be?"

"She's not a trollop. She's an addict, and right now she's in **peril**. I've got to find her before the police do."

"Ah, now that's the challenge, isn't it? If time is of the essence, the rate goes up."

"The rate? Can't you just help me for old time's sake, dude? Think of how many times I helped you out of a jam."

"You were always better at intricating yourself into jams than **extricating** others from them."

"There's no such word as *intricating*, Squeeze."

Squeeze frowned. "Cash, smartass." He unclipped his portable money changer from his belt. "Give it up, narc," he said, tapping the money changer.

Jaden sighed. "How much?"

"Two months' salary."

"A trifle **exorbitant**, don't you think?"

"It's the going rate."

"One month."

Squeeze smiled. "You still have plenty of street left in you, Amsterdam. One month it is."

Jaden transferred the money to Squeeze. He barely had enough to cover it.

"So take me to her," Jaden said.

"Never heard of her."

---

leer: creepy or suggestive look

trollop: promiscuous woman

peril: danger

extricating: removing

exorbitant: excessive

"What the blast! You said you knew where she was!"

"I said nothing of the sort, my boy. I simply said finding her in a timely fashion would be difficult."

"You **bilked** me! Not a smart move, bro. I could have the cops down on your fat face in about five minutes."

"I somehow doubt you'll do that, Amsterdam."

"Try me."

"Relax, Amsterdam, I was just messing with you a little. I'd be happy to point you in the right direction. What's this girl's poison? Drugs? Alcohol? Sex?"

"Music."

"A raver, eh? That'll be easy enough. Only one really big party going on tonight. I'll take you there."

"Get in," Jaden said. "I'll drive."

"We'd better walk. It's the only way to get there without calling attention to yourself and me. And if you're going **incognito** you'd better cover up."

"Cover up what?"

"Your plate, doofus," Squeeze said, throwing him the grimy maroon derby from his head. "Don't want to broadcast the fact that you're a splitter. The cybernetics give you away."

Jaden reached for his own cap in his jeans pocket, but it was gone. Must have fallen out in the struggle with Ally. Reluctantly, Jaden took the hat Squeeze offered and pulled it over his dreads. It had a **rancid** smell.

Squeeze led him through the back streets of the old Port Authority on Tampa Bay. Surrounded by monotonously similar, **obsolete**, no longer used ships and abandoned warehouses, Jaden had no idea where he was or where he was going.

Finally Squeeze stopped at a rusted-out fuel tanker.

"What on earth would she be doing here?" Jaden asked.

Squeeze took a dark object from his pocket. Jaden heard a crack

---

bilked: cheated   **rancid:** rotten   **obsolete:** outdated
incognito: in disguise

and a pink halo **enveloped** Squeeze. He tossed Jaden the **lumines-cent** rod. "Hold this in front of you and say 'Ibiza' as you walk into the tanker."

"Then what happens—I smash my face into the tanker and you laugh your ass off?"

"If you want to find your girl, say the word and walk in," Squeeze said.

"I don't know," Jaden said, holding the glowing pink rod in front of him. But it wasn't like he had much of a choice. Taking one last deep breath, he strode forward.

---

enveloped: covered completely

luminescent: glowing

"Ibiza," Jaden said, holding the glowing pink rod in front of him and stepping into the wall of the tanker.

The world **shimmered** and glitter rained down on him.

"Welcome to Joy Island!" called a **chorus** of unseen voices. A **boisterous** girl with pink hair and a plastic dress pulled him into the largest group of bobbing, weaving, dancing teens and twenty-somethings he'd ever seen.

The **strident**, repetitive beat of the music drowned out almost everything else. The air **reeked** of sweat and alcohol as a fine mist of fog filtered down from above him—a playground for **refracting** lasers.

The spectacle of thousands of **carousing** neon-clad teens was nothing compared to the more powerful **assault** on his senses. Every last person in the tanker was an addict, and the swirling colors of their addictions **pummeled** him from every side.

Confounded by what he was seeing, Jaden reeled. He couldn't understand it. He wasn't jacked in to any of them, yet he saw each addict's obsession as **lucidly** as if it were his own. It had to have something to do with the music. The pounding, repetitive beat **reverberated** in his skull, and the images that floated before him seemed to pulse with the rhythm.

He blinked, trying to relax, but the rave continued to **assail** his senses. Even when he closed his eyes, he saw the throbbing mass of addicts before him. He had to get out of there. "Bathroom!" he yelled to the girl with the pink bob. She pointed at a **dingy** door off to the side. Jaden charged inside and crumpled against the paper towel dispenser, trying to force the images from his brain.

---

shimmered: softly sparkled
chorus: group of voices
boisterous: rowdy or in high spirits
strident: loud and harsh
reeked: stank

refracting: bending like light rays
carousing: drunkenly celebrating
assault: attack
pummeled: pounded
confounded: confused

lucidly: clearly
reverberated: echoed
assail: attack violently
dingy: dirty or shabby

A dozen addicts in neon garb crowded the sinks and three stalls. One bent over a sink counting out pale orange pills from a plastic bag. Her mind swirled **verdant** with gold spheres and pink cubes. He'd have recognized the addict by those cues alone, but the blueberry-colored pigtails confirmed it.

"Ally!" he cried.

Ally didn't look up. She had finally **extricated** a pill from the plastic bag and held it between her thumb and forefinger.

"Stop it!" Jaden shouted, lurching over to slap the pills from her hand. They scattered across the filthy floor between high heels and sneakers of the other ravers.

Ally scurried after the pills. "Gotta get my groove back," she mumbled. "Gotta dance, gotta move. Gotta get my groove back."

Jaden lifted her up by the shoulders. "What have you done?" he asked her.

A **beatific** raver peeing in the corner called over his shoulder. "Let her go, man. She's following her **bliss**. . . ."

"She's high as a kite!"

"Yeah . . . " the peeing raver agreed **wistfully**. "Too bad it's only for a couple of hours, huh?"

"Yo, Ally," Jaden said, dragging Ally toward the door. "We're getting outta here."

"Will you dance with me?" she asked, wrapping her arms **languidly** around his neck and leaning into him.

He loved the closeness of their bodies, the scent of her sweat-misted skin, the way the tips of her fingers brushed the back of his neck. Struggling to maintain his **equanimity**, he **disentangled** himself from her, afraid his **palpitating** heart would reveal his true feelings. "I can't do that, Ally."

"Then I'm not going with you," she said, folding her arms. Her lower lip protruded in a stubborn pout, and he felt something give way inside of him.

---

verdant: green	**bliss:** complete happiness	**equanimity:** calm
extricated: removed	**wistfully:** sadly and with longing	**disentangled:** unraveled
beatific: looking completely happy	**languidly:** weakly	**palpitating:** beating fast

He couldn't resist her.

"All right, all right . . . we'll dance then. Let's just get out of this bathroom."

"Hooray!" Ally **exulted**, hugging him and putting a candy necklace around his head like a **lei**.

Jaden took a deep breath, squeezed Ally's hand and plunged out of the restroom. The tumbling images of the addicts' obsessions **bombarded** him all over again. The exit—he had to find the exit.

The **ingress** he had come through seemed to have **dematerialized** and was nowhere to be found. Ally pulled him into the **chaos** at the center of the dance floor, bobbing and wheeling the entire time.

The rave was arranged like a huge wheel with the dance floor in the center and assorted archways radiating out around the **circumference** like spokes. One of those had to be the way out.

Ally **undulated** to the trippy beats, and Jaden stared at her, fascinated. Finally, he tore his gaze away and looked around. He had to find a way out, and concentrating on that would be a lot tougher if he let himself take in just how appealing she was right now.

They passed through the nearest archway and found themselves in an **ornate** casino, complete with every virtual and physical gambling racket imaginable. Wheels spun, cronies hunched over their chips, and cool operators gazed **placidly** over their cards. How on earth had they gotten everything in here without the police noticing? Jaden traced the **perimeter** of the casino, Ally in tow. No exit.

Jaden pulled Ally into the next archway. This one was a bar with drinks that were obviously not of the milk-and-cookies kind. A handful of couples swayed on the bar's dance floor, but mostly they just drank.

The next archway contained **corpulent gourmand**s gorging themselves at a **lavish buffet** unlike any Jaden had ever seen. It wasn't the normal chopped and processed overcooked foods. The buffet brimmed with crab legs, steaks, and other **viands** of the highest

---

exulted: rejoiced
bombarded: attacked
ingress: entrance
dematerialized: disappeared
chaos: complete confusion
lei: hawaiian floral necklace

circumference: the edge of a circle
undulated: moved like a wave
ornate: overdecorated
placidly: calmly

perimeter: edge
corpulent: fat
gourmand: person who enjoys food
lavish: extravagant or rich
buffet: meal on a table
viands: food

quality. The **wafting** odor made Jaden forget the addicts for just a moment. His stomach growled, and a good chunk of him wanted to join in on the **gluttony**.

The next archway led them to an **ostentatious** bordello. Scantily clad men and women lounged across chairs and benches with their best **wanton** "come hither" looks adorning their **comely** faces. Several eyebrows raised at the sight of Jaden, and more than one addict sought to catch his eye.

Ally seemed **oblivious** to all the addictions. As long as she could hear the music, she tuned everything else out. Jaden pulled her back to the main dance floor, leaving the **debauchery** behind. Was there no way out?

Off to one side, the cheer of "Welcome to Joy Island!" rose momentarily above the **commotion**. If there was a way in, there had to be a way out. He tried to ignore everything else and listen only for the welcome **salutation** to Joy Island!

There it was again! Jaden dragged Ally in the direction of the cheer and waited as Ally **cavorted**, spraying glitter and sweat with every movement.

A third cheer erupted, this time close enough for Jaden to see the raver enter. He kept his eyes locked on the spot along the wall and pulled Ally along with him. He clasped the glow stick Squeeze had given him and wrapped Ally's hands around it as well.

"Ibiza!" he **intoned incisively**, and walked into the rusty wall of the tanker.

"One way!" a raver shouted. "Over there, man!" The raver pushed the pair toward a different segment of wall. Surprised and off-balance, Jaden tumbled through what he thought was solid steel.

He and Ally landed on their stomachs on the dirty **wharf**.

The music **abated**, as did the colors and sounds of the addicts. Blissful silence **encompassed** Jaden, soothing him. He lay there for

---

wafting: floating on air
gluttony: greed or overeating
ostentatious: showy, pretentious
wanton: mischievous or lustful

comely: attractive
oblivious: unaware
debauchery: corruption
commotion: disturbance
salutation: greeting
cavorted: pranced
intoned: said in singing tone

incisively: directly and decisively
wharf: where ships discharge passengers and cargo
abated: subsided
encompassed: surrounded

just a minute, **relishing** the feeling of peace.

Ally's experience was clearly just the opposite.

"Where's the music?" she cried. "I have to have my music!" She jumped to her feet and charged toward the tanker.

Jaden let her go, but there was nowhere for her to go *to* anymore. He was getting a bit weary of having to babysit a seventeen-year-old. He put his hand on her arm and tried to turn her toward him.

She jerked her arm away. "Not again, you monster," she said, cowering. Her eyes had the same haunted, **tortured** look as when she fled the bungalow. "A person comes to you for help, and you turn into Narcenstein or something."

Jaden's hands dropped. "Ally, wait. I'm sorry about that. I shouldn't have done it. That's why I came after you—to tell you I'm sorry. But seeing you taking some drug on top of raving . . . well, how do you expect me to react?"

"It's not 'some drug.' It's Joy."

Jaden winced. "I know you like it, but you're not in your right mind," he pleaded.

"That's where you're wrong. It's only when I'm on Joy that I am in my right mind. If it hadn't been for Tymur popping by with a little hit when I got back from T.D.C., I'd have never even remembered that I wasn't in my right mind."

"So the name of the drug you're taking—it's Joy?"

"Uh-huh," she said, nodding. "It makes me whole again." Ally yawned. "I'm sleepy." Her eyes drooped.

Jaden looked around. Nothing of any use, just some rusted junk and **discarded** crates. This wasn't a safe place to sleep.

"I need a nap," she said, intent on **repose** regardless of her surroundings. She crumpled where she stood.

Jaden helped her to a crate near the edge of Tampa Bay. Open on two sides, it provided protection from the elements and a clear view of any potential **interlopers**. Jaden helped her down and she

---

relishing: enjoying
tortured: anguished

discarded: thrown away
repose: rest

interlopers: intruders

fell asleep. Jaden took off his jacket and covered her, wrapping his arms around her for warmth and security.

Even asleep she was beautiful. Actually, he noticed it more than ever now that she was so still, so **tranquil**. He brushed a stray hair from her forehead. What was going on in that head of hers? What made her so **susceptible** to addiction? Did he have the same thing inside of him? A summons to a **latent** obsession?

He wanted so badly to reach into her mind, to see what the drug Joy was really doing to her. It would be so easy. He had his **satchel** with the portable splitter equipment. With her sleeping, he wouldn't even need to immobilize her. He'd be able to slip right in and out again, and she'd never have a clue.

No. He couldn't. He *wouldn't*. He had to regain Ally's trust after what he did to her, and **penetrating** her mind while she was asleep was not the place to start.

Still, he wondered about Joy, wondered what it did, precisely, in a person's body. It was clear now that the drug was responsible for exploding the walls that splitters built around people's addictions. But where did something like that come from? Who would have created it without The Corporation knowing? Nothing got done without the knowledge and approval of The Corporation. It just didn't happen. To create a drug like this, they'd need significant scientific resources and **copious** amounts of cash, neither of which most people had. Not even Senior Management types.

And it wasn't just the drug. Who could have put together such a large, virtually invisible black market for it? There had always been a black market for addictions. That's how he had made his **livelihood** back in the old days, dealing drugs and booze to the low-life scum on Nebraska Avenue. That was before music and other addictions that weren't Corporation-approved became illegal. Now there must be this huge black market machine peddling Joy to rekindle people's addictions and then selling them the vice of their choice. How had that

---

tranquil: peaceful
susceptible: impressionable or vulnerable
latent: potential

satchel: small bag
penetrating: piercing

copious: plentiful
livelihood: means of support

happened, and when? It had to be recently or else Ally wouldn't have been his first repeat patient. But it was obviously **propagating** quickly, since after seeing Ally his waiting room had been packed with repeat patients yesterday. How could something like this go unnoticed?

He should **divulge** it all to somebody, someone in charge. Senior Management would know what to do.

Ally sighed and turned in his arms slightly, snuggling closer against his chest.

Jaden shuddered. Telling Senior Management about Joy would mean he'd have to tell them about Ally, too, and then she really would be pink-slipped. He'd gone through too much to let that happen to her.

Jaden held Ally tight throughout the cool tropical evening, keeping an eye out for revved-up ravers who might be in the market for a quick score. The night passed peacefully, and the sun rose early, casting a warm glow across Tampa Bay.

Ally's eyes fluttered open. She gazed up at him and her eyes grew wide when she realized whose arms she was in, but she didn't pull away. "Pretty sunrise," she said.

"Uh-huh," Jaden said, stroking her hair with no intention of diverting his gaze from her to the sunrise.

In silence she watched the sun **gild** the horizon.

"Thank you for watching over me," Ally said softly. She arched her back and slid up his lap, turning slightly to face him.

Jaden felt each breath that escaped her warm, full lips. His heart caught in his chest as he looked at her, a rush of emotion swirling through him.

Ally slipped her hand around his neck, her nails lingering just beneath his earlobe. He tingled at her touch. She lifted up and gently pressed the nape of his neck.

Jaden leaned in, and as Ally's eyelashes trembled shut, their lips met.

---

propagating: reproducing   **gild:** paint with gold
divulge: reveal

He let out a soft groan, the sensation of kissing Ally shutting out everything else. He drifted his arms around her waist just as he felt her pull back.

"I knew you'd take care of me," she murmured.

"What if I hadn't?"

Ally turned and nestled down into his arms. "But you did. You were my knight in shining dreadlocks."

"But what if I hadn't ridden up on my white horse, Ally? Seriously bad things could have happened to you." He couldn't believe how **heedless** she was of the real danger she had put herself in last night.

She wiggled in his lap, her eyes still closed. "Knights always rescue the **damsel** in distress."

Jaden frowned. This was an act—the same **servile vulnerability** she had put on for her father the night he caught them sneaking in after curfew—all bouncy and accommodating to keep from getting in trouble.

Was he being played? Had he been all night long?

"If I hadn't come along tonight you just would have gone off with some other guy."

She flinched. "Oh, come on now, Jaden. Tell me what you really think."

Every part of him was telling him to stop, but he couldn't seem to hold the vicious words in. "As high as you were, I could have been anyone, any welcoming two arms to hold you."

"No, that's crazy. Jaden, I knew it was you all along. I wouldn't have gone with anyone else."

"You almost didn't go with me," Jaden said. "I had to drag you out."

"That's because the first thing they teach you about Joy is to never leave the rave high. Everyone is safe at the rave."

"All those strangers make you safe?"

---

heedless: thoughtless or unconcerned
damsel: young girl

servile: slavelike

vulnerability: capable of being hurt

"That's not the point. The rave is a contained environment. The drug wears off in a few hours and the walls around the addiction go back up, mostly. There's just enough of a little hole, a crack really, that lets the craving **seep** through. You crave your addiction, sure, but you crave Joy more. You want that tiny little **fissure** to become a **gully** and let the pleasure wash over you. You want to feed the need."

He paused, her words sinking in. "But when I split you at the Detention Center, there wasn't anything but a tiny bit of your addiction wall left."

"Because I was high. You split me when I was still coming down. That's probably why it didn't work."

"And you let me do it anyhow?"

"Yeah, sure. I mean, what could it hurt? Even if it had worked, another hit of Joy and the wall would have been down again."

"So if Joy brings the wall down, why did you want me to split you?"

"Hey, I'm not always high. When you come down off of Joy, you come *really* down. I was **despondent**. Wanted it all to end, I guess."

"So the entire time I'm freaking out thinking I'm losing my powers, you've known exactly what's wrong?"

"What made you think you were losing your powers?"

"You did! I couldn't treat you. I couldn't fix you, no matter what I did. You let me think I was a failure."

"Nobody could ever think you were a failure, Jaden. You're my knight."

"Well you can go find yourself another one, you little raver-girl," Jaden said, turning his back on her, getting up, and strutting purposefully in the direction of what he hoped was his car.

Ally ran after him and grabbed his arm. "Don't be like that, Jaden. I never—"

---

seep: ooze   **gully:** small valley or gulch   **despondent:** gloomy
fissure: crack

Jaden pulled his arm away. "Get away from me, Ally. I'm warning you. Friends don't do what you did to me. I don't want to see you anymore."

Marching forward, he left Ally Fayre quietly crying in his **wake**—he hoped for good.

---

wake: track left behind

Jaden crept back into the Splitter Center, hoping everyone was still asleep. In the one stroke of **serendipity** in the last twenty-four hours, they were. His hair had matted flat on one side and stuck out sideways on the other. His body smelled of stale beer, sweat, and smoke. He didn't care. He'd eventually have to deal with Kim's **wrath** over the missed bed-check, but the night's adventure had worn him out, and sleep **beckoned**.

He had scarcely closed his eyes when his door slid open.

"Go away," Jaden said, burying his head under his pillow. "I'm sick."

"You'll be feeling better soon," Kim's **effervescent** voice chimed. "You made the next cut. Sergeant Mack—"

"Call me Truck," a low, **gravelly** voice spat.

Jaden peered out from beneath his pillow. A tall, burly man in a black ripper uniform stood stiffly at the foot of his bed. He wore his blond hair shaved like Reth and had an even stronger, square chin. A long scar was carved into the left side of his face.

"Sergeant Truck is here to interview you for the position," Kim finished.

"Really?" Jaden asked. "When?"

"Now, boy!" Truck **bellowed**, chuckling.

"You'll need to be in the exam room in ten minutes," Kim said curtly. "Don't make us wait on you." They turned and left.

"Dammit!" Jaden muttered his **malediction** to the closed door. He couldn't get a break.

With his mouth tasting like the side of that rusty tanker, Jaden stumbled into the shower. He had to get the **noisome** odor of the

---

serendipity: unexpected good fortune
wrath: strong anger
beckoned: summoned or attracted

effervescent: bubbly or lively
gravelly: rough or raspy
bellowed: shouted in a deep voice

malediction: curse
noisome: bad-smelling or harmful

city off of him and get into some more appropriate clothes. He had no time to shave, and he brushed his teeth in the hall on the way. On zero hours of sleep and with a mouth full of hastily swallowed toothpaste, Jaden reeled into the interview room.

Of course Reth, **punctilious** as always, was already there. He chattered **solicitously** with an older gentleman, nodding his head at all the right times.

Jaden swallowed hard. Director Cameron was going to oversee the interview. It was bad enough that the panel was filled with the twin auditors who hadn't been the slightest bit **laudatory** with him; Sergeant Truck, who had seen Jaden at probably his worst moment in years, and Director Cameron, who put a whole different spin on things.

The **redoubtable** Director Cameron was the head of the entire Tamlando area, not just the little old Splitter Center. If Jaden ever had hopes of being promoted, they depended on that man.

Jaden slid quietly into his seat. He felt **woozy** from the lack of sleep and found it hard to focus on the clock behind the panel, much less the panelists. To his surprise, Kim also joined the group. Jaden didn't know if having Kim on the panel would be a **boon** or **bane**. He'd find out soon enough.

One of the auditors took the role of first **inquisitor**. "So tell us why you think you're the best person for the Ripper Squad position."

Reth jumped in immediately. "As you know, the Warren family has a history of producing outstanding splitters and rippers. Six generations now. It's in my genes. It's truly all about **heredity**, if you want to get the best man for the position."

Pencils moved furiously across the computer tablets in front of the panelists. Everyone except the director took careful notes.

"And you?" the second auditor asked Jaden. "Why do you think you're the best person for the job?"

---

punctilious: careful
solicitously: anxiously or protectively
laudatory: expressing praise

redoubtable: formidable or worthy of respect
woozy: dizzy
boon: benefit

bane: curse
inquisitor: someone who questions harshly
heredity: inheritance

"**Prowess**," Jaden answered **succinctly**. "It's not about what other people have done. It's about what I can do, and have done, in my current position. My record speaks for itself."

The twin auditors didn't show any expression. Jaden wasn't particularly **deferential**. He didn't much care what they thought of his answers. Once they found out what he had done, creating the portable splitting equipment, not reporting a **proscribed** operation, not to mention missing bed-check and putting the needs of individual people above that of The Corporation, he'd never get the job anyhow. He'd play their games for now, but he could say or do whatever he wanted. He'd never get the job.

Truck spoke next. "So why do you want to be part of my team?"

Reth launched into a **dissertation** about the golden record of Truck's department, about Truck's history as a brilliant ripper and leader. **Fervent** and specific, Reth sounded sincere, even though he was obviously sucking up to the sergeant. There was no question in Jaden's mind that Reth was going to get the job.

"And you, boy? Why do you want to be part of my team?" Truck **blustered**.

"I don't know that I do want to be part of your team," Jaden replied smoothly.

Kim gasped at his response, and the twin auditors scribbled on their tablets. "I just met you," Jaden continued, "and I judge people based on their specific experiences with me, not some write-up in a file. But I can tell you this. I want to be a ripper. I want to help the worst offenders, the **dregs** of society, become the very best employees they can be. I can't imagine a more honorable **vocation** nor one I'm better suited for."

The interview continued on for over an hour, with Reth giving textbook-perfect answers to the questions while Jaden could only muster **flippant** responses. Reth was **indomitable** and obviously had the job. The **eminent** Director Cameron even shook Reth's

---

prowess: bravery or extraordinary ability
succinctly: expressing precisely
deferential: showing respect and esteem

proscribed: prohibited
dissertation: extensive piece of writing
fervent: impassioned
blustered: spoke loudly or boastfully

dregs: leftover parts
vocation: occupation
flippant: glib or disrespectful
indomitable: unconquerable
eminent: famous

hand as he left.

Depressed and exhausted, Jaden returned to his room. Years of hard work down the drain, and all because of a **vacuous** girl. He fell asleep across his **rumpled** covers and dreamed of blueberry-colored hair.

He awoke to the sound of someone rapping on his door. "Pizza delivery!" the voice called. "Pizza delivery for Jaden Emory!"

Jaden punched the door open. "I didn't order any pizza."

The pizza delivery person wore a cap with a long visor that shaded the eyes. "You've got one anyhow, bucko," the delivery person said, stepping into Jaden's room and shutting the door behind.

The pizza delivery person whipped off the cap and a cascade of blueberry-colored locks fell down.

"Ally!"

"Happy to see me?" she asked **genially**.

"What are you doing here?" He knew he should still be mad at her, but the minute he saw her warm smile and sparkling eyes, he couldn't stay angry. Still, he had to try. "Patients aren't allowed in the splitter dorms," he said **gruffly**.

"Is that all I am to you, Jaden? One of your patients?" She looked **demurely** down and then up again into his eyes.

He turned away. "You're not even that to me, anymore. I've washed my hands of you."

Ally **flitted** around to face him. She took his hands in hers. "I don't think so," she nearly purred, her fingers tickling his.

Jaden warmed at her **alluring** touch, the sensation of holding her in his arms all night surging back through his body. He pulled his hands away.

"You can't bounce in here and make everything okay. You have no idea what you put me through."

Ally softened, her tone no longer **pert**. She sat down on the bed and patted the space beside her. "Then tell me. We never talk."

---

vacuous: stupid	**gruffly:** roughly or sternly	**alluring:** attractive or
rumpled: crumpled or wrinkled	**demurely:** modestly or coyly	charming
genially: graciously	**flitted:** moved erratically	**pert:** cocky and lively

He sat down next to her. "This isn't the appropriate **forum**. You shouldn't be here."

"Then meet me somewhere, tonight. We'll talk." She rested her hand on his leg. Jaden felt a blush rise to his cheeks but he didn't move away.

"Why are you like this?" he asked.

"Like what?"

"Like this. One minute you're all **affable**, the next you're in addict-mode, and the next you turn all **callous**. I don't understand you."

"It's just the way I am."

"Do you want to be that way?"

"I don't know. Sometimes yes, sometimes no. I love my passions. It's what makes me, well, me."

"You can't be part of my life like this. You're messing up my world."

"Isn't that what love does? It messes up everything until you don't know which way is up, but all in all, it's a wonderful ride."

"Who said anything about love?"

"I did, just now. Isn't it obvious that's what's happening between us? You're the only person who has ever really cared about me. Not my parents, not my teachers, and certainly not The Corporation. I'm totally falling for you, Jaden Emory, and I think you're falling for me, too." She looked up at him with her big aqua eyes, **entreating** for an **affirmation**.

He didn't know what to say. In his heart, all he wanted to do was hold her in his arms and tell her how much he wanted her. He wanted to stroke her hair, feel her soft lips against his again. She was so tempting . . .

But no. He couldn't do it. He couldn't forgive her for what she'd put him through. He'd probably lost the ripper job because of her, or would once they found out about his and Ally's **exploits**.

forum: public meeting	**callous:** hardened and	**affirmation:** confirmation or
affable: pleasant and	unemotional	validation
friendly	**entreating:** pleading	**exploits:** feats

The warmth of Ally's hand spread through his thigh. This was all just so wrong. He felt as if he was being played yet again.

"Jaden?" she **exhorted**.

"Get out."

"What?"

"I'm not going to be played again, Ally Fayre. I'm done doing your bidding." Even Jaden was surprised at his words. Every fiber in his being still wanted to reach for her, to hold her. But that was exactly why he had to push her away, the sooner the better.

"Is that what you think this is about? Me trying to get you to do something for me?"

"You can stop pretending. I'm done with you. I want you out of my life."

Tears tumbled down Ally's cheeks.

"Jaden—"

"Just go."

Without another word, Ally tucked her hair back under her hat and left.

* * * * *

The smell of the pizza drew Baqer out of his lab like a mouse to cheese.

"Pepperoni?" he asked, poking his head into Jaden's room.

Jaden shrugged. "Help yourself."

Baqer opened the pizza box. "How cute," he said **sarcastically**.

Jaden looked at the pizza. All the pepperonis were arranged in the shape of a heart. He sighed. "It's from Ally."

"A thank-you gift for last night?" Baqer asked, taking a slice of pizza from the right lobe of the heart.

"We didn't, I mean, I didn't—oh, man . . . " Jaden didn't even know where to begin.

---

exhorted: urged strongly   **sarcastically:** ironically or bitterly

"Easy, my friend. Have a slice."

The thought of consuming a piece of pizza representing Ally's heart made Jaden want to **retch**. He shook his head.

"She's an addict and wants to stay that way. I didn't get a chance to try to help her with our equipment, and I won't. I'm done with her." He took the duffle bag out from underneath his bed and slid it toward Baqer.

"Bummer," Baqer said, his mouth filled with gooey pizza. "Guess you won't be wanting this, then—"

"Take it," Jaden said grimly.

*   *   *   *   *

Jaden brooded in his room the entire day and into the evening. He didn't even come out for dinner. Ally was eating away at his soul, bit by bit. He had to tell someone, but whom could he trust? Not Reth or any of the other splitters, and when he had the chance to tell Baqer it hadn't felt right. Who else was there? Maybe he should go and see Ally, one last time.

No, no . . . that was his problem. He had to get her out of his brain.

A knock echoed on his door.

"Catch me later," Jaden called through the door.

"But the Groundhog's Day court is open now," came Kim's perky reply. She opened the door and walked into his room. She wore a skintight bodysuit, ready for exercise. "Look, I know you're **disheartened** about your performance in the interview today, but you didn't do all that bad. Really."

Jaden sighed. Here he was **moping** about Ally, and he had totally forgotten the interview that had **abrogated** all hopes of promotion for him. Great.

"You just need to blow off some steam," Kim said. "Grab your

---

retch: vomit   **moping:** thinking gloomily   **abrogated:** nullified
disheartened: discouraged

gear and let's head for the gym."

Maybe Kim was right. He needed to stop feeling sorry for himself and just get out and do something. "You're on."

When they arrived at the Groundhog's Day court, it was still empty. Groundhog's Day was a sport in which two players wielded enormous mallets and tried to hammer down four-foot-high groundhog robots that popped up out of holes in the court. Jaden considered Groundhog's Day to be among the many stupid facets of the culture he lived in, but he had to admire Kim's prowess at the game. After two hours of intense competition, Kim **eked** the final victory, having smacked down seventy-five of the robotic rodents to Jaden's sixty-four.

"Feel better?" Kim asked, wiping her face with a towel and tossing a second one to Jaden.

"Yeah," Jaden said, and he meant it. The game had been so action-packed that he realized he hadn't thought of Ally once in two whole hours.

And yet, here he was, his first **respite** thinking about that girl again. How was he ever going to get her out of his mind?

"You okay?" Kim asked, touching up her makeup even though they were both going to have to hit the showers. "You look like something's on your mind."

"Someone," Jaden said.

"Oh, yeah? What's up?"

Jaden looked at Kim's sincere **countenance**. She had been his team leader and **confidante** since the day he first arrived at the Splitter Center, a scared kid, **rife** with troubles. And here he was again. He'd always been able to trust her in the past.

The entire story flooded out of him. It felt purifying to let it all just pour out without **censure**, knowing Kim would understand. When he was all done, he took a deep, cleansing breath. "Well?"

Kim's look wasn't judgmental or stern, but it was **resolute** and

---

eked: got with difficulty
respite: break
countenance: face

confidante: someone trusted with secrets
rife: abundantly supplied with

censure: condemnation or reprimand
resolute: determined

firm. "Jaden, you're an addict."

"*What?*" That was the last thing he'd expected. He knew he'd made all kinds of stupid mistakes because of Ally, but he wasn't like her—he wasn't an addict to music, to Joy, or to anything else.

"That girl. She's **enthralled** you. She's got you under her spell. I knew you hadn't been yourself these last few days, and now I know why."

Jaden frowned. "I know I've been off a few days, but to call me an *addict*, isn't that a bit strong?"

"Look at your behavior and answer your own question. Are you acting like a productive employee?"

"Not the last couple of days—"

"And what's been causing your **aberrant** behavior?"

"Ally," he said softly, hating to admit it to even himself.

"Do you want your life to continue on like this?"

"But I've quit. I've given her up."

"And how many of your addicts have you heard say that, Jaden? How long will your determination last, without assistance?"

Jaden knew she was right. He'd seen addict after addict try it on his own. They all eventually came for treatment.

"It's not that bad," Jaden insisted.

"And if you take care of it now, it never will be," Kim said. "You've got too much going for you, Jaden. You must be **diligent**. Make it stop now, and you'll be able to go on with your life."

"But how? You can't split a person out of you."

"She's an addiction just like alcohol or music. She can be split."

"But if I undergo splitting, won't The Corporation know? It'll tank any hopes I have of the Ripper Squad."

"Not if we go tonight. We'll pop down to the Splitter Center, take care of you, and no one will be the wiser."

"But who will do the splitting?"

"I will. I was a splitter before I was a team leader. It's **requisite**

---

enthralled: cast a spell on   **diligent:** hardworking   **requisite:** necessary
aberrant: atypical

for the job. I'm sure my skills haven't **atrophied**."

"I can't ask you to do that. If we got caught, you'd get in trouble too."

"We're not going to get caught." She put her arm around his shoulder. "Trust me."

The Splitting Center seemed **ominous** at night. Only the nighttime safety track lighting glowed in the darkened halls. Every step echoed on the cold tile floors.

"You know the procedure," Kim said, gesturing toward the splitting chair. Jaden turned his wrists as Kim locked the safety straps around his arms, legs, and head. The chair adjusted around him, molding itself to his body like quicksand. He felt the cold feet of the probe rise from the chair and rest on the back of his neck. A sharp prick and then he felt the probe's tongue slide beneath his skin.

Once his thoughts were connected to Kim, he'd see what she saw, and maybe he'd finally get to experience the **palette** of his own mind. He'd always been curious. He thought maybe he was a royal gold, or even amethyst purple.

Instead, he got blackness, and the vague feeling of being watched. It was as if someone was standing just over his left shoulder, sorting through his open brain **cavity**.

Stop, he tried to say, but nothing came out of his mouth. His thoughts felt like cold fingers wiggling after grapes buried inside cherry gelatin. But there was something else inside the gelatin, something darker and colder. Whatever it was, he knew it wasn't his. The coldness invaded his mind, and he shivered against the restraints. The coldness rose up from the base of his brain, encompassing everything.

Then, as swiftly as it had arrived, the feeling of being watched **dissipated**. The cold remained.

A voice **traversed** the darkness. "We're all done, Jaden."

Jaden opened his eyes, seeing and hearing as if his body was

---

atrophied: wasted away   **palette:** range of colors   **dissipated:** subsided
ominous: threatening   **cavity:** hollowed-out space   **traversed:** crossed

under water. "Great," he heard himself answer.

"Wasn't that bad at all, was it?" Kim asked.

Jaden shook his head, and a wave of **nausea** rolled through him. "Nope," he heard himself say. He willed his body to stand up and felt as if he might collapse back into the chair, but his body gave no outward **indication** of his weakness.

"Tell me how you feel about that girl," Kim said.

"Which girl?" Jaden asked, feeling as if he was surfacing through **balmy** tropical waters, leaving something cold and hard buried beneath him.

"That girl—Ally Fayre."

"Oh, you mean that addict I need to pink-slip first thing tomorrow," Jaden answered, feeling himself burst through the waves.

"Exactly," Kim said, grinning.

---

nausea: stomach upset or extreme distress

indication: sign or expression

balmy: mild

"I don't want to go," Jaden **protested**.

"As your team leader and your friend, I'm telling you that you've got to have closure on your relationship with that girl," Kim said.

"But Fort Miami is so far away," Jaden said. "And I've got patients who need me—"

"And it's all just excuses and you know it. It's your last chance to see that girl before she gets **interred** in the Unemployed Zone for the next ten years. You'll regret it if you don't go. I won't allow it."

"But I don't ever even think about her, unless you bring her up," Jaden said truthfully. "I don't need closure on something I never have to deal with."

"All the same, I'm ordering you to attend. She's being interred tomorrow. You can ride with Reth if you'd like. He never misses Internment Tuesdays."

"Thanks, but I'll pass. I'll take my stupid flying—I mean, I'll take my Phoenix 5000 instead."

The next day Baqer caught him in the hall on the way to the parking garage. "Want company?" he asked.

"Okay," Jaden said **ambivalently,** not entirely certain that he did. "I'm going to Fort Miami."

"I know," Baqer said.

"Won't be back until after dinner. That okay?"

"Of course."

Jaden had anticipated a quiet **excursion**. Baqer never was very **garrulous** but evidently he decided to make an exception today.

"I was sorry to hear about Ally," Baqer piped up soon after they'd started driving.

---

protested: objected
interred: buried

ambivalently: with contradictory feelings
excursion: expedition or outing

garrulous: talkative

"She's an addict. She got what she deserved."

Baqer raised his eyebrows. "Harsh, my friend. Listen, I know you're angry now, but if you want to talk, you can always come to me."

"Talk about what?"

"It's hard to talk about feelings, I know, but it's important to try when something this big happens. It's not good to keep it all bottled up. Believe me, I've been there."

"I'm not bottling anything up. I really don't have anything to talk about." He didn't know what Baqer was trying to **elicit** from him. Maybe his friend was trying to get something off of his own chest. "But you know, if you have something you want to share, go ahead. I'm glad to listen. I do it pretty well," he said, smiling.

Baqer shook his head **morosely**. "I know it's only been a week, but with these speed-trials, everything goes so swiftly. It's like when my mother died. She had been sick for so long, but when she finally gave up the ghost, it happened so quickly. . . . "

There it was, Jaden thought. **Stoic** Baqer finally wanted to talk about his mother. "I understand what you mean," Jaden said.

"I thought you would," Baqer said, **lapsing** into silence for the rest of the trip.

Jaden used the upper **barrier** to the Unemployed Zone to guide him to Fort Miami. The fifty-foot tall fence that **circumscribed** the U.Z. and divided it from the free world stretched clear across the southern tip of Florida, along what used to be the Tamiami Trail, U.S. 41. Flight paths had taken the place of intercity and interstate roads, and as a result, many of the old highways lay in **disrepair**. Nobody used old U.S. 41. Nobody wanted to think much about the 1.5-million-square-mile prison that made up South Florida.

Jaden tried to fly low, hoping to catch a **glimpse** of the criminals behind the wall. The **arid** land was flat and grassy with very few trees and less water, a **savanna** on the edge of the large swamp of the Everglades. Criminals were few and far between in that **morass**.

---

elicit: draw forth
morosely: gloomily
stoic: unemotional
lapsing: sinking or slipping

barrier: obstacle
circumscribed: surrounded
disrepair: needing repair
glimpse: brief view

arid: dry
savanna: plain or grassland
with few trees
morass: swamp

Groups of **nomads** seemed to **congregate** at various **intervals** along the wall. Jaden figured the groups **signified** food and supply distribution centers.

He'd never been to Fort Miami or the Unemployed Zone, but he knew a little bit about the U.Z. He knew criminals were given food and supplies at regular intervals, allowing them to survive in a rather **inimical** environment, just barely above the level of **privation**. The swamps bred mosquitoes in the summer and alligators and poisonous snakes all year round. The savannas were **mercilessly** hot, particularly now in the summer with only minimal **foliage** to provide shade from the heat. The southern tip of the U.Z. enclosed the Florida Keys, a string of once-connected islands now **accessible** only by boats constructed by the criminals. The Keys were **hospitable** enough, if you could avoid the pirates.

The entire U.Z. was managed by Fort Miami to the east. The only way in or out was through the gates of Fort Miami. As they circled the free air space waiting for a security code for the parking garage, Jaden took in the enormous **scope** of the installation. A series of connected buildings, it stretched for miles along the barrier to the Unemployed Zone. Some of the buildings served as holding cells for criminals awaiting trial. Some processed addicts. Others warehoused provisions for prisoners. Thousands of pounds of food entered the U.Z. each day just to sustain the criminals. He saw a low, flat building and wondered if that might be the barracks for the Ripper Squad. They were stationed at Fort Miami, **primed** to work with the most incorrigible addicts.

It had been over a week now since Jaden's disastrous interview to become a ripper, and he hadn't heard a word. His only **consolation** was that Reth hadn't heard yet either, so there was a chance the job was his. Still, he couldn't imagine how that would be possible after the mess he'd made of everything. All because of his stupid addiction to

---

nomads: wanderers
congregate: assemble
intervals: with spaces in between
signified: meant or implied
inimical: unfriendly

privation: deprivation
mercilessly: brutally
foliage: leaves and flowers
accessible: reachable

hospitable: welcoming
scope: range
primed: prepared
consolation: comfort

Ally. The girl had probably cost him the job he'd been working toward for so long.

A large crowd had already **congregated** around the walkway to the main gates of the U.Z., waiting for the new batch of prisoners that would pass through the elevated platform off to his left. This gated tunnel reminded Jaden of a hamster's Habitrail tunnel. It suited the addicts. They were all just animals who couldn't **quell** their urges anyhow.

Jaden and Baqer jostled through the crowd, trying to find a spot where they'd have a good view of the prisoner walkway. The **assemblage** was a mixed bag. Small groups of grieving family members were **interspersed** with gleefully judgmental employees, eager to see new addicts behind bars.

A row of olive-clad guards filed out to line the walkway between Fort Miami and the U.Z. A **chant** rose from the U.Z. side of the wall, soft at first, and then louder as a chorus of hundreds of addicts **clamored**, "Fresh meat! Fresh meat!"

"Hey, Emory! That's what your girlfriend's about to be in three minutes: fresh meat!" Reth's voice rose above the anxious **din**. Jaden spotted him pushing through the crowd, grinning. Kim had said that Reth always came to Internment Tuesdays, but Jaden had hoped to avoid him by coming separately.

"She's not my girlfriend," Jaden said.

"Tough to maintain that long-distance relationship, huh?" came Reth's **riposte**.

Jaden rolled his eyes.

"I feel sorry for you, Emory. You finally get a girlfriend and some jerk pink-slips her. What a shame."

"I turned her in," Jaden said, without a sliver of **compunction**.

Baqer almost swallowed his tongue in shock.

"Yeah, right," Reth said.

"I did. She was an incorrigible addict and deserved what she got.

---

congregated: gathered together
quell: subdue or pacify
assemblage: gathering

interspersed: mixed
chant: words used repetitively
clamored: loudly insisted

din: loud noise
riposte: retort or quick reply
compunction: qualm or moral doubt

I'm the one who pink-slipped her."

Reth seemed more convinced by Baqer's **stupor** than by Jaden's sincerity. Maybe he should have told Baqer, but it just didn't occur to him. He never thought about that girl unless someone else brought her up.

Reth arched a **skeptical** eyebrow, then clapped Jaden on the back. "Congratulations, mate! You might make a decent employee after all!" He laughed, and Jaden joined in with his **cackle**.

"It's all about justice, Jaden," Reth continued. "People need to get what they deserve, no more, no less. If they break the rules of The Corporation, and step outside of **prescribed** policy, they need to get pink-slipped, plain and simple."

"The Corporation's rules are very important," Jaden **conceded**. He tried to ignore the weird expression on Baqer's face. What was he so bent out of shape about anyhow?

The criminals filed **tentatively** across the platform. A cheer went up from the crowd, nearly drowning out the **wailing** of **distraught** relatives. Hecklers **jeered** the criminals, and Jaden and Reth joined in.

Baqer grabbed Jaden by the shoulders. "What are you doing?"

Jaden jerked back. "What's your problem?"

"Jaden, Ally is about to go to jail for ten years, and you're cheering?"

"Sure, why not? They're all getting what they deserve." Jaden **craned** his neck searching the faces of all those incorrigible addicts, each one unique. He wondered what stories they hid behind their **bland visages**. Maybe he'd get to find out if got the Ripper Squad job.

Baqer blocked his view. "Jaden, you don't feel that way, or at least you didn't last week. You wanted to save her, remember?"

Jaden shrugged. "She couldn't be saved. What's the big deal?"

"She is," Baqer yelled, pointing at the blue-haired teen on the platform. Ally paused, **balking** at the large crowd. Someone threw a shoe at the cage right next to her, and she jumped and screamed.

---

stupor: daze	**tentatively:** hesitantly	**craned:** stretched
skeptical: uncertain	**wailing:** lamenting or crying	**bland:** dull
cackle: harsh laugh	**distraught:** distressed	**visages:** faces
prescribed: ordered	**jeered:** taunted or made fun of	**balking:** blocking or refusing
conceded: admitted		

Torrential laughter tumbled through the crowd.

"Fresh meat! Fresh meat!" came the **obstreperous** cry from the other side of the wall.

"Squeeze the blueberry!" Jaden shouted.

Reth echoed him, and then together they shouted, "Squeeze the blueberry! Squeeze the blueberry!"

The girl followed the sound of the cheer and met Jaden's gleeful gaze. He waved to the **pitiful** addict. Bye, bye, little addict. Hope the rave was worth it.

Baqer didn't talk to him the whole way home, which was fine by him. He'd had enough of the **vexed** lab tech's **derisive** comments. When they returned to the Splitter Center, Jaden took Reth's offer to play a few rounds of SimRipper. The virtual reality game trained real rippers and gave potential rippers a taste of what the job was like. Two players or more could compete against one another and a virtual ripper opponent to see how many criminals they could treat in a certain time period. SimRipper was calibrated for rippers with full ripper cybernetics, so Jaden and Reth both had to work doubly hard at the game. Splitter cybernetics were no match for rippers. They almost always lost to the virtual ripper, but practicing was fun. It made them both productive employees.

Kim's voice issued from somewhere behind them. "What are you two boys doing?"

Jaden checked his score. A slim number of points separated him and Reth.

"Jaden Emory and Reth Warren, talk to me!" Kim insisted petulantly.

No time to pause the game now.

"Player three has entered the game!" the computer **proclaimed**.

The round ended and a session of daily departmental activity followed. But this time there was a new employee onscreen—a blue-haired Kim who was even **lither** than the one in real life, if

---

torrential: violently rushing
obstreperous: unruly and noisy

pitiful: arousing pity or contempt
vexed: irritated

derisive: mocking
proclaimed: declared
lither: more supple

that was possible. Jaden couldn't help but **gape**, and he noticed that Reth **gawked** as well.

"Is this the only way I'm going to get you boys to pay me any attention?" she pouted.

"I believe there's something different about you, Kim," Reth said, his tone very serious. "New dress?"

Jaden laughed. "No, no, Reth . . . she had corrective surgery on her eyes. See? No more glasses."

Reth guffawed and Jaden joined him.

"You two are too much! What's gotten into you?"

"Splitters are allowed to joke," Jaden said.

"Yes, but you two aren't exactly **renowned** for your **camaraderie**."

"You're going to **chastise** us for playing nice?" Jaden said.

"No blasted way," Reth agreed. "Jaden just grew a couple today, that's all."

In the simulation, Jaden punched Reth playfully in the arm and Reth scowled, making Jaden's social skills score drop a couple of points.

"Hey, you knew that was a joke!" Jaden complained.

"Yeah, but this way I make a little **headway** at your expense. Gotta learn how to play the game, guy."

Kim rolled her eyes and logged out of the game.

Jaden and Reth finally paused the game two hours before bed. Jaden tried to get himself declared winner, but Reth refused, despite the fact that Jaden was slightly ahead, so they compromised by putting the game on pause.

After such a busy day and evening, Jaden thought it would feel good to just **sprawl** across his bed and relax a bit. His bed felt lumpy, though, and when he moved to his favorite chair, he found that it leaned a bit to the right. No matter how hard he tried, he couldn't get comfortable anywhere. Something was wrong, but he couldn't figure out what it was.

---

gape: stare with his mouth open
gawked: stared stupidly
renowned: famous

camaraderie: friendly spirit
chastise: punish
headway: progress

sprawl: lie with limbs spread out

Maybe he just needed a good burst of late-night shopping. He still had forty-five minutes until bed-check. He could pop into his nifty Phoenix 5000 and be over at the Ybor City Mall in five, shop for a half hour, and be back with five minutes to spare. That would feed his need.

Even after that hefty bribe he'd had to give Squeeze to find Ally, he still had a **plenitude** of credits on his card. Everyone knew you had to spend money to make money, so perhaps his emptiness was a result of too much cash flow.

At the mall, **incessant** virtual ads **inundated** Jaden. Instead of setting his filter for his most restrictive preferences, he left the setting as it was and caved to most of the sales pitches. He picked up his purchases near the exit and caught sight of an unwelcome **specter**. Squeeze leaned outside one of the mall restaurants, a new, equally filthy purple derby cocked on his head. He shook hands with a jittery-looking woman who **palmed** a glow stick and a packet of what Jaden assumed was Joy.

He shuddered at the thought of the drug. One little pill could undo all the hard work of the entire Corporation. Who could have come up with something so **nefarious**?

Squeeze winked and tipped his derby at him.

Jaden turned his head. He left the mall with his arms full and his heart empty.

---

plenitude: abundance
incessant: not stopping

inundated: flooded or overwhelmed
specter: ghost

palmed: handed stealthily
nefarious: evil

Jaden returned home as he had planned, just before bed-check. Unfortunately, the late-night shopping spree hadn't boosted his spirits. As he lay in bed, **amorphous** darkness all around him, his ghosts came to visit. Each time he closed his eyes Squeeze was there. It was as if with that one wink Squeeze said, "I'm always here for you, Amsterdam, if you want her back."

And each time he saw Squeeze in his mind, he thought of that girl, of Ally, and something cold and dark turned over inside of him.

Jaden knew what the problem was. It must still be bothering him that he didn't know where Joy came from. Who had created such an evil, subversive drug without The Corporation knowing? It just didn't seem possible. Everyone worked for The Corporation—everyone from the corner grocery clerk to the primary school teachers to the CEO. How could someone achieve something of this scale outside The Corporation?

Well, he'd never find the answer **sequestered** in his room. He'd have to do a bit of **reconnaissance**. He'd start with that lowlife Squeeze. He'd probably get busted for sneaking out after bedcheck, but he didn't care. This was more important than getting written up for some **frivolous infraction**. If he could find the source of Joy, he'd be a hero.

Squeeze wasn't as easy to find as he had been last time. With the mall closed, Jaden checked Squeeze's normal haunts, but they were all **bereft** of activity. Squeeze worked the streets, but that didn't mean he had to be on them all the time. Jaden had been disconnected from the darker side of Tamlando for so long that he didn't have the connections he used to. Maybe his car gave him away, and the seedier

---

amorphous: shapeless
sequestered: separated or segregated

reconnaissance: looking for information
frivolous: unserious

infraction: violation
bereft: deprived

elements took cover whenever he approached. After all, his model-year Phoenix 5000 didn't exactly blend in. He decided to hoof it, to take the streets by foot, like he had in the old days. He'd start down by the docks where Squeeze had taken him when he was looking for Ally.

After two hours haunting the alleys and loading docks of Tamlando and paying off tipsters, Jaden found himself outside a **derelict** warehouse on Tampa Bay. He stood on a box to peep in the window. Squeeze was there all right, but so were at least half a dozen other thugs.

Jaden felt a hand on the back of his shirt as he was hustled from his **perch**.

"Hey, boss! Look what I found!" The unseen **thug** dragged Jaden into the warehouse.

A large toad of a woman waddled forward. "Well, now that you've brought him inside, we'll have to kill him," she said, taking a bite of a rapidly melting ice cream bar.

"Wait!" Jaden said. "What do you think I've seen? Some boxes and some warehouse stuff? Doesn't seem like something to kill a guy over. I just came to see Squeeze."

One of the thugs hit Squeeze upside the back of his head. "You led him here?"

Squeeze shrugged. "It's just some kid I used to know. 'Bout as special as a coconut in the U.Z."

"Looks like a narc," the round woman said, taking another bite of her ice cream bar. Chocolate peeled off the outside and dripped down the front of her shirt.

"I'm just a kid," Jaden said, echoing Squeeze's words.

"You don't look like you're just a kid," the boss said.

Jaden had an idea. "I came to buy some Joy. I need a hit, really bad."

The tension in the room **diminished**. Shoulders slouched, hands

---

derelict: run-down
perch: high spot
thug: gangster or killer
diminished: lessened

moved away from guns. A couple of the thugs even snickered.

"Not too smart to be an addict, I see," the toad woman said. She nodded at Squeeze. "Give him his hit and get him out of here. Now."

"Yes, ma'am. Right away," Squeeze said **obsequiously**, skittering toward Jaden. He handed him a glow-key and a packet of two little orange pills. "Five hundred," Squeeze said.

"For this?" Jaden said.

Squeeze squinted at him through heavy eyelids. "Five hundred," he repeated, then lower, "Pay and get the hell out of here before they change their minds, Amsterdam."

The thugs eyed him. One rested his hand on his gun again.

Jaden transferred the credits into Squeeze's account on the spot, palmed the drugs and glow-key and left.

What a bust. Sneaking out, **traipsing** all over the scummy side of town, for what? He wasn't a single step closer to finding out who was behind Joy. It was obvious even when he did get Squeeze alone, the weasel wouldn't know anything. He was just a **pawn**—a gofer for a boss who was probably just a pawn herself. What a waste of time.

He reached into his pocket and pulled out the glow-key and the pills. He should just toss them into the bay, dump them where they couldn't hurt anyone.

Jaden plopped down at the edge of the water, his feet dangling over the side of the dock. Those little pills were outstanding at hurting people, at ruining lives. He opened the wax paper packet and tapped the two little orange pills into his palm. Little pills like these had gotten that girl pink-slipped.

The cold hard stone in his gut turned over.

That girl had a name—Ally. And the pills hadn't gotten her pink-slipped. He had.

He shoved the pills back into the envelope and stuck them in his

---

obsequiously: subserviently   **traipsing:** wandering   **pawn:** something used by another

pocket as he bolted back up from the edge of the water.

If he hadn't pink-slipped her, someone else would have. It was all for the best. The sooner she served her time and learned the error of her ways, the sooner she'd be able to be a productive Employee of The Corporation again.

He couldn't **ruminate** anymore. It was late, and he had to get back. He didn't even know why he was thinking about Ally anyhow. He had been split by a professional, and that should be the end of it. He couldn't help but blame Squeeze. His mind had associated the dealer with that girl, so every time he saw Squeeze, he thought of her. Blast him!

Jaden followed the line of the harbor along the water, hoping to recognize some through-street that would lead him back to his stupid flying car. A warm tropical breeze wafted across the water, but suddenly a chill curled his spine. He looked up.

The rusted oil tanker where he found Ally **loomed** in front of him.

Dammit! Wasn't he ever going to be able to put this behind him?

He rapped on the **defunct** tanker with his fists. It echoed mournfully. He kicked it and flecks of **iodized** metal showered off the tanker like bits of orange glitter.

He took the glow-key from his pocket and threw it at the tanker. It wasn't as if he'd be needing it.

The glow-key issued a soft crack and fell to the ground, glowing pink. The wall of the tanker **wavered** as if it were made of water and someone had dropped a pebble into it.

He bent over to pick up the glow-key, and the pills fell out of his pocket. Obeying some urge he didn't even understand, he put one of the pills in his mouth and swallowed it. He shivered.

Suddenly, he crumpled to the ground, struggling to hold back the tears, his dreads falling in the dirt. He missed her so much.

Just thinking the words made him feel both better and worse

---

ruminate: think about repeatedly
loomed: appeared in exaggerated size

defunct: no longer existing
iodized: treated with iodine

wavered: fluctuated or moved like a wave

at the same time. Now he knew what the cold hard stone in his gut was. It was Ally, and he had put her there when he doomed her to ten years in the Unemployed Zone. He'd do anything to have her back, to break down the wall that kept him from the girl he loved. Yeah, she'd been right about that. He didn't know how or why or when it had happened, especially so fast, but it was true. He loved Ally.

He closed his eyes and saw Squeeze winking at him again. "I'm always here for you, Amsterdam, if you want her back."

He did. Now. Forever.

He picked up the glow-key, held it in front of him, and intoned, "Ibiza!"

The tanker shimmered and opened for him as glitter rained down from above.

"Welcome to Joy Island!" arose the cry.

It was just as he had remembered it, the writhing ravers, the loud, rhythmic beat music, the soft mist of fog with **oscillating** lasers. But something was different. The addictions of the addicts no longer pummeled him. The music **infused** him with **ardor**, energy, excitement, and, well, joy. He couldn't contain himself. He let the music take him, and he danced amid strangers, bouncing and whirling in an **arbitrary choreography** using his glow-key as his partner, and yet he didn't feel alone. He felt a great **affinity** with this group of **anonymous** strangers, more than he ever did with The Corporation. As an employee you were always part of the big picture, part of the greater business plan, but in an **antiseptic** kind of way. Every employee was connected to every other employee, but only as titles on an organizational chart. This was so totally, completely different.

He felt united with every person around him, but in a personal, spiritual way. For once in his life he felt he was truly experiencing the moment, living in the now, and not planning and scheduling for some **ambiguous** future. *This must be what Ally felt when she was*

---

oscillating: fluctuating
infused: filled
ardor: passion
arbitrary: random

choreography: dances or movements
affinity: attraction or likeness
anonymous: unnamed or unrecognizable

antiseptic: orderly and cold
ambiguous: able to be understood in more than one way

here, he thought. It must be why she came here, even though she knew it meant the end for her.

Ally. Ally Fayre. She was no longer "that girl" in his mind. She was Ally, the girl he loved, the girl he wanted, the girl he needed as much as he needed food or air.

"I'm in love with Ally Fayre!" he shouted, even though he knew it wouldn't rise above the din of the music. "I love her!"

The cold hard stone in his gut exploded outward with his words, and he knew that it was right, that it was fixed, that he was the way he always should be.

Except he didn't have Ally. It wasn't the music or the drugs giving him this indescribable feeling, it was his love for Ally. His addiction was back, and he welcomed it.

But he couldn't **savor** his joy without the object of his **idolatrous** obsession. All around him gamblers placed bets, drinkers drank, and food addicts gorged themselves to excess. He needed his addiction, too. He must feed the need.

Jaden raced out of the rave and found his **resplendent** red Phoenix 5000. He tumbled behind the wheel and fumbled with the keys. He knew just what he had to do. He had to find Ally, to be with her. It was the only way.

He soared high above any normally used flight pattern and **charted** a course straight for the Unemployed Zone. The answer was simple. His Phoenix was a high-flyer, and fast. He'd zip right over the fence and take one last peek at his love. At near top speed it took less than half an hour to reach the edge of the Unemployed Zone. Flooring the pedal on his stupid flying car, Jaden soared straight for the U.Z.

---

savor: enjoy
idolatrous: blindly worshipful

resplendent: shining brilliantly

charted: mapped

Jaden awoke to the coppery taste of blood and the **noxious** smell of smoke. The Phoenix 5000 was crumpled around him. He felt an **acute** pain in his right knee and saw a bit of blood seeping through his pants, but his wounds weren't **exigent**. His immediate concern was the black smoke **billowing** out of the rear of the car. Flames licked through the smoke.

And people thought flying cars were a good idea.

Maneuvering with his good leg, he twisted until his back was against the door and pushed. Broken glass and pointed metal **jabbed** into his spine, but the door creaked a bit. If his knee wasn't busted open he'd just scoot out the window, but he was afraid he'd **exacerbate** his injury.

The flames licked higher. He had to get out of the stupid car.

Readjusting his position, and using the steering wheel to help him, he pushed again. The door gave just a bit more. He'd have to use both feet to free himself.

He screamed as the pain shot through his body. The door screeched and groaned, but it finally spat him out onto the grass with the other **debris**.

The flames crackled, sending slivers of hot glass into the night. Jaden scooted away from the car beneath the shelter of the only significant coverage around—a short, scraggly saw palmetto with razor-sharp palm **fronds** and a spiny trunk.

How on earth could he have been so stupid to try to fly into the Unemployed Zone? He'd known about the force field, but Joy had messed with his brain so much that he had forgotten everything but Ally. Only the pain of his wounds had brought him back to some

---

noxious: harmful
acute: sharp or severe
exigent: requiring immediate aid

billowing: swelling out or rolling
maneuvering: cleverly managing
jabbed: stabbed or punched

exacerbate: make more severe
debris: fragments or rubbish
fronds: large leaves

semblance of normalcy. The ache for Ally, though, remained.

Forget flying into the U.Z.; what had he been thinking when he took Joy to begin with? He knew what it did to people, what it did to Ally. Had he been that close to his **nadir**?

The hairs on the back of Jaden's neck stood up. He was being watched. An animal, maybe? Did alligators come this far out of the swamp? Or maybe a Florida panther? He didn't think there were still bears here, but something was definitely looking him over.

He peered into the darkness. Two eyes glowed back at him.

"You okay, mister?" came the hushed voice. A boy.

"What do you think?" Jaden snapped, wincing at the pain.

A **wiry** boy of maybe eleven or twelve stepped out of the shadows. The firelight crackled, reflecting the fragile fence. The boy stood on the Unemployed Zone side of the barrier.

"I think you better scoot away from that palm and a little closer to that fire, if you want to keep snake-bite free. Cottonmouths aren't so keen on fire, but they are mighty partial to curling up in those palmettos."

"Ah, thanks," Jaden said. He scooted back toward the **conflagration** and winced.

"Hurt bad?" the kid asked, searching him with intelligent, **inquisitive** eyes.

Jaden tenderly touched his shoulder. It spiked pain through his upper body.

"Yeah," he gasped. He either had **contusion**s from the seat restraint or his collarbone was broken. When his breathing returned to normal, he asked, "What are you doing out here, kid?"

"You mean 'in' here, don't you? You want to know why I'm in the U.Z."

"I meant out here alone, at night."

"I take care of myself."

"I see that," Jaden said, smiling. The kid's **irreverent** attitude

semblance: appearance	**conflagration:** fire	**contusion:** bruise
nadir: lowest point	**inquisitive:** extremely	**irreverent:** disrespectful
wiry: lean and energetic	curious	

reminded him of his own at that age.

"Better bandage that knee," the boy said. "The perims will come for you, but probably not until sunrise. Nobody comes out here at night."

"The perims?" Jaden asked as he tore the sleeve of his shirt to create a **compress** to cover the wound and **curtail** the bleeding.

"Perimeter guards. Better have a good story by then if you want to stay on that side of the fence. **Ailing** auntie in Fort Miami, or a depressed friend on the eve of his wedding or something."

Again, the **astute** kid was right. He'd have to come up with a cover story for why he slammed into a force field. Hopefully the guards wouldn't come for him too quickly. He needed the Joy to be out of his system. The aching hole in his heart when he thought about Ally confirmed the drug was still in full force. "What's your name, kid?"

"They call me Tail, 'cause I'm always waggin' around for scraps."

"Doesn't everyone get daily **rations**?" Jaden asked.

Tail laughed. "You obviously don't know much about the life of an In. Unless I'm swift and use a **ruse** or two, my rations get taken. What I can manage to save mostly gets used as payment for services. There's not much left to actually eat."

Jaden appreciated the kid's **guile**. He wished he had something for the **intrepid** boy, but even if he did, he'd have no way of getting it to him.

"So it seems you get around a bit, huh?"

"Yeah, some."

"Ever see the new prisoners come in?"

"Every week," Tail said. "Easy marks."

"Do you remember yesterday's batch?"

"I'm Unemployed, not **daft**," the kid said.

"There's one particular girl I'm interested in. Her name is Ally Fayre. Have you seen her?"

"Don't know any names. What's she look like?"

"Blue hair, in pigtails probably. Short, **petite**, aqua eyes."

---

compress: folded cloth pressed against a body part
curtail: limit or reduce
ailing: sickly
astute: shrewd or clever

rations: food allowances
ruse: trick
guile: deceitfulness

intrepid: fearless
daft: crazy or silly
petite: small-figured

"Blue hair, huh? She a raver?"

"Yeah, that's her."

"Heard the new batch of ravers already got the thumb," Tail said, wagging his hand like a hitchhiker seeking a ride. "Whole bunch of bodies got dumped along the edge of the 'Glades. Any that were alive are probably alligator bait by now. You will be, too, if you don't bandage that leg. They can smell blood a mile away."

Jaden heard Tail's warning, but he couldn't process anything after the news that the girl he loved was dead. Ally was dead. The night closed in around him, and he felt his throat tighten. It couldn't be true, it just couldn't.

A spotlight broke through Jaden's **grief**. A silent, unmarked black aero-truck hovered silently about forty feet above him.

"Prisoner will leave the perimeter immediately," boomed a voice from the Raptor 300.

Tail turned instantly and **sprinted** away from the fence, arms and legs pumping hard. Evidently he had been through this drill before. Must be the perimeter guards from Fort Miami. But he'd have thought the truck would have had some sort of markings.

Suddenly Jaden remembered the small envelope of Joy still in his pocket. Whoever had come for him, he couldn't let that be found on him. He could take it, but he needed as much of his wits about him as he could. He'd have to hide it.

The Raptor 300 began landing maneuvers.

Jaden slipped the pill envelope out of his pocket and slid his hand behind him, almost beneath him. Trying not to look suspicious as the Raptor 300 landed not twenty-five feet from him, Jaden squirreled a hole into the sandy earth. He pressed the envelope into it and covered the hole back up. The grass was spotty at best, so with a bit of effort nobody would notice the disturbed square of Florida sand. The glow-key was missing. He figured he'd lost it on the dance floor. If not, it would **combust** in the

---

grief: sorrow **sprinted:** ran fast **combust:** burn

fire. Either way he was relatively safe.

The doors of the Raptor 300 slid open and a group of masked, black-**attired** soldiers **brandishing** state-of-the-art weaponry surrounded him.

attired: dressed

brandishing: shaking or waving threateningly

Jaden **blanched**.

The soldiers parted and two **austere** men in expensive navy suits and mirror shades approached. "Jaden Emory?"

"Yes?" Jaden squeaked.

The man reported into the com link on his wrist. "Target acquired. Initiate clean-sweep sequence oh-six-ten." He turned to the broad-shouldered soldiers. "Get him inside the Raptor."

Two soldiers set down a stretcher and rolled Jaden onto it. Pain seared through his body, but he stifled everything but a **grimace**.

Other soldiers encircled the car, extinguishing the flames. Man, he hoped that glow-key had **incinerated** completely.

An armored vehicle rumbled out of the **cavernous** cargo hold of the **ebony** Raptor. Soldiers collected the remnants of his crash and put them in back. What the hell was going on?

The night sky became the brushed steel of the Raptor's cargo hold. The stretcher jolted into a combat med-station. One masked soldier examined his knee, while another prodded his shoulder. Neither **administered** an **analgesic** for the pain.

"What the hell did you think you were doing?" a familiar voice demanded from behind.

Jaden looked up with pain-glazed eyes and found Kim scowling down at him. "What's going on?" he asked.

"You sneak out of the Splitter Complex after bed-check and then crash your Phoenix 5000 into the U.Z.? I think I'm the one who gets to ask the questions."

"I went for a drive, that's all. I couldn't sleep."

"Right."

---

blanched: turned pale
austere: severe
grimace: disgusted or pained expression

incinerated: burned to ashes
cavernous: like a large cave
ebony: dark like ebony wood

administered: performed or dispensed
analgesic: painkiller

"Kim, it's the truth." He wasn't **mendacious** by nature and was **loath** to lie to her after all she'd done for him, but he couldn't tell her what had really **transpired**. He just couldn't.

Kim narrowed her eyes. "So why'd you crash?"

Focusing on the blinking panel of lights above him on the med-station, he avoided her gaze. "I guess I was more tired than I thought. I must have **dozed** at the wheel negotiating the return trip."

Raising a skeptical eyebrow, Kim didn't reply.

The soldier working on Jaden's knee dug beneath a bone. Jaden stifled a cry. "Who are these people? What are they doing here?"

"Isn't it obvious? They're cleaning up after your mess."

"But why?"

"The Corporation can't have one of our star rippers found trying to **infiltrate** the U.Z."

"Don't **jest** with me, Kim."

"I'm not. Word came after bed-check. You made it into the Ripper Squad." She flipped her long platinum hair behind her. "I thought I'd be **magnanimous** and wake you up with the good news. When I did, I found an empty bed."

The medic working on his leg had stopped the bleeding and now bandaged the wound.

Jaden tried to process the news that he'd actually landed the job that had been his only dream for so long. He knew he should be thrilled, but there was so much else going on it was hard to focus.

"But how'd you find me?" he asked her. "I didn't even know where I was going until I got here," Jaden said without a smidge of **veracity**. He didn't like the thought of Kim knowing where he had been, particularly in light of his **manifold indiscretions** last night.

"Corporation tracking devices are embedded in every vehicle. You forced me to use it. I couldn't let you **tarnish** the name of the Tamlando Splitters on the eve of your promotion."

"But I just went out for a drive!" Jaden protested. He had the

---

mendacious: dishonest
loath: reluctant
transpired: took place
dozed: slept lightly
infiltrate: enter or pass through

jest: joke
magnanimous: noble
veracity: truthfulness or accuracy

manifold: diverse
indiscretions: imprudent actions
tarnish: dull or stain

sinking feeling that Kim knew more than she was telling. If a Corporation tracking device tracked him here, had it also tracked him scouring the **disreputable** part of town for Squeeze?

"And look what happened."

"It was an accident. I was tired." Jaden's hands balled into fists. He didn't appreciate being **vituperated** even though he knew she was right.

"The Jaden I know wouldn't have taken a nose dive into a force field, no matter how **enervated** he was. You'd better shape up, Emory, or you're going to find it hard-going on the Ripper Squad. Sergeant Truck won't be nearly as **tolerant** as I've been."

A bass voice thundered from behind Kim. "Damn straight I won't!" Truck strode over to the med-station. His black uniform matched that of the soldiers outside, but he didn't wear a face mask. Even if he had, Jaden would have identified the solid wall of a man anywhere.

"I'm sorry, sir. It won't happen again. I'll be on my best behavior."

Truck's **resonant** laugh **blindsided** Jaden. "Hold on, soldier. Don't turn into some lightweight or you'll never fit in with my department. We work hard. We play hard. You get one get-out-of-jail-free card. You've just used yours. Remember that, and you'll do fine." The well-tanned wrinkles around Truck's eyes crinkled.

"Yes, sir." The medic shifted Jaden's shoulder again, and he **flinched**.

"Get this kid a shot of pain meds," Truck barked.

"Yes, Sergeant," the masked medic answered.

Jaden felt the welcome prick of the **sedative** and a warmth like honey **disseminated** through his veins. He strained to focus on Kim.

"I'm sorry," he **murmured**. "I didn't want any of this to happen." The honey oozed across his brain and the world drifted away.

* * * * *

---

disreputable: not respectable
vituperated: scolded
enervated: made weaker
tolerant: allowing or accepting

resonant: echoing
blindsided: unpleasantly surprised
flinched: winced or recoiled

sedative: calming drug
disseminated: spread throughout
murmured: spoke softly

Jaden awoke in his bed back at the Splitter Complex, naked except for his underwear. Man, he hoped Truck had put him in bed and not Kim. He sat up **gingerly**. His shoulder ached and his knee throbbed, but he could use them both. He stood and found he could even walk without too much of a limp. The few minor **lacerations** would heal in no time. He couldn't have gotten better care in a hospital.

Jaden's luck had been **providential**. Not only had he survived the crash that should have killed him, he'd gotten the job for which he'd **yearned**. He had no idea how he had gotten the job and not Reth, or why having this job wasn't making him feel everything he'd expected to feel. This was his dream, and he was still a mess of confused emotions inside. One thing was certain, though. He was definitely going to **gloat** to Reth.

He didn't know how long before he'd transfer to Fort Miami, but he figured he'd better be ready. He wasn't about to let Kim and Truck down again. As he boxed away his trinkets, he realized how little of it he wanted to keep with him. Most of it would have to go into storage for the time being anyhow. The barracks didn't have much room for personal effects. Eventually he might be allowed to move off-base, but not for the first year.

Probably his most precious possession was his h-pod, a camera that took three-dimensional, holographic pictures. He kept the palm-size **orb** permanently tuned to the hologram he took during last summer's trip to the Disney Entertainment Complex in eastern Tamlando. Kim had scheduled a team-building exercise for all the splitters and support staff. As they entered the complex, his department had stopped to **mug** for a **tableau** in front of the Cinderella Castle. Reth wiggled bunny ears over Kim's blonde crown of hair. Jaden wore his sunglasses and folded his arms across his chest, flashing the h-pod his coolest look. The other Tamlando Splitters all attempted similar goofiness. Most of the support techs had been

---

gingerly: very carefully
lacerations: cuts or tears
providential: lucky

yearned: longed
gloat: brag triumphantly
orb: circle or sphere

mug: pose or make faces
tableau: scene

crowded into the back row, and Baqer would have barely made it into the scene if Jaden hadn't pulled his friend next to him. Baqer had been uncomfortable in the spotlight and had kept his eyes cast downward, though a **bashful** grin did creep up his cheeks.

As Jaden wrapped up his h-pod and put it in the small box of effects he planned on taking with him, he tried not to think what Baqer must be thinking about him right now. He'd treated his friend horribly, and there was no way Jaden could explain away his poor behavior at Internment Tuesday without telling him about Joy. He'd just have to avoid Baqer for a while—until time had a chance to soften the wounds.

"Trying to get first dibs on my room, Emory?" Reth leaned against the door frame.

"Get out." He turned his back and continued packing. He didn't have time for some prejudiced **dilettante** who had to harass prisoners just to make himself feel better.

"What's gotten into you? I figured you'd be emotional about how the Ripper Squad turned out, but no need to bite my head off."

Jaden shook his head, his dreads flapping about his face. How could he feel such **enmity** toward Reth when they had **taunted** the new prisoners together only days before? The heat of a blush rose to his cheeks as the **hypocrisy** of his actions hit him.

Dammit! Joy—it had to be Joy. It must still be in his system, mucking about with his brain. He'd have to try to pretend to be the person he was before he took Joy, if he wanted to keep his **nocturnal** adventures a secret.

In an attempt to be **conciliatory**, Jaden turned and sat down on his bed meekly. "I'm sorry. I guess I'm just a bit on edge. It's a big deal, you know?"

Reth moved a box and sat backward in Jaden's desk chair. "I know. But there are other good jobs out there—stuff besides the Ripper Squad."

---

bashful: shy
dilettante: dabbler or amateur
enmity: shared hatred

taunted: made fun of
hypocrisy: self-serving inconsistency

nocturnal: active at night
conciliatory: pleasing or reconciling

"Yeah, definitely." Jaden stood up and took an autographed Groundhog's Day mallet down from the top shelf. He put it in one of the boxes for storage. "I must say, you're taking this all in stride."

"Well, it really was **inevitable**.

"I was certain you were a ringer."

"Thanks."

"I mean it. I'm **elated** I made it, but I'm **appalled** that you didn't."

Reth arched an eyebrow. "Excuse me? I got my notification this morning."

Jaden blinked. Wait a second, what was the story here? They couldn't both have gotten the job—there was only one opening. "But I—I heard the same thing. This, uh, this morning, too," Jaden lied. He didn't like the **duplicity**, but there was no way he could tell Reth the circumstances under which he had really been told.

"I was trying to be nice about it Emory, but if you're going to be a jerk—"

"I'm serious. I made it into the Ripper Squad."

"We'll see what Kim has to say about your lies," Reth said, storming out.

"Not without me, you aren't," Jaden said, following. He was just as eager to **ascertain** the truth as Reth was. Dammit, what if everything he thought had happened was just some post-crash **delusion**? What if he wasn't really going to be a ripper after all?

Reth burst into Kim's office without knocking. "Tell this boll weevil that I'm the new Ripper Squad member."

Jaden was glad Kim would be their **arbiter**. She'd set him straight.

"Reth, you're the new Ripper Squad member," Kim said with a **devious** grin, "and so is Jaden."

"What?" Jaden exclaimed.

"No way," Reth said, shaking his head. "He's not good enough."

---

inevitable: unavoidable	**duplicity:** deception	**arbiter:** judge
elated: joyous	**ascertain:** discover	**devious:** sneaky or sly
appalled: deeply shocked	**delusion:** false belief	

"Sergeant Truck thought otherwise. He wanted you both, put in the **requisition**, and got you. You'll get your ripper upgrades this afternoon, and then you're to report to Fort Miami tomorrow."

"Tomorrow?" Jaden asked. He'd wished for this day for years, but to abandon everyone and everything he knew so quickly?

"I know *I'll* be ready," Reth said **arrogantly**.

Still in shock at the speed of recent events, Jaden reported to Baqer's lab, **anxiety** pumping through his veins.

"Kim sent me for ripper upgrades," Jaden said, hoping Baqer wouldn't bring up his **reprehensible** behavior.

"Sit," Baqer said.

Jaden's knee still bugged him so he slid carefully onto the stool.

Baqer prepped him in silence, setting an array of tools and materials on the chrome tray on the lab table, including the pale gold ripper plate that would replace his chrome splitter one. Jaden could tell that Baqer, who was even less talkative than usual, was still holding a grudge.

"Will it hurt?" Jaden asked, more to break the silence than out of curiosity.

Baqer didn't look up, but his voice carried a **vitriolic** edge. "Probably."

"Great bedside manner," Jaden said tensely. He didn't know which made him more anxious, being **estranged** from his best friend or having someone who was that angry with him about to take a scalpel to his skull.

Baqer huffed in response, his breath stirring Jaden's **tousled** dreads.

"Just joking," Jaden said. "Geesh."

"Don't like your sense of humor."

Jaden had the distinct feeling Baqer was talking less about his joke and more about the cruel way he had **heckled** Ally at the internment ceremony. At the time, Jaden had found it hilarious. Now the

---

requisition: official demand
arrogantly: proudly and overbearingly
anxiety: nervousness

reprehensible: deserving blame
vitriolic: biting
estranged: separated

tousled: tangled or rumpled
heckled: harassed

memory of his behavior heated his shame.

Jaden clamped his mouth shut for the rest of the operation. Silently, Jaden **pined** over the loss of someone so important to him. He should just apologize to his friend and be done with it, but his shame held him back. He was afraid their friendship was **irrevocably** damaged.

The hour dragged on **interminably**. Finally Baqer set down his last probe and pulled off his latex gloves. "We're done," he said, his words a death **knell** for their five-year friendship.

Unfortunately, my friend, I'm afraid you're right, Jaden thought as he slunk from the lab.

*　　*　　*　　*　　*

The next morning, Jaden tried not to fidget as he and Reth waited in Truck's **sterile** office for the sergeant to return. Didn't look like he spent much time in it. Long-overdue paperwork overflowed a wire basket on his desk. The personal effects that decorated most employees' desks were noticeably absent. On the wall, a framed photograph showed Truck stiffly shaking hands with some important-looking suit in front of The Corporation flag.

As the minutes ticked by, Jaden repeatedly wiped his palms on the pants of his gray ripper trainee uniform in an unsuccessful attempt to keep them from sweating.

Reth, on the other hand, kept his **sangfroid** as always, as if he were waiting for a train that was always on time. He never once fidgeted. He even slumped in the chair as if he was bored with the entire affair.

The door burst open and Truck blustered in, first shaking Reth's hand and then Jaden's. "Sorry I'm late, fellas. Let's get out of here and I'll introduce you to your new department." He tossed another folder of paperwork onto the stack and ushered them into the hall.

---

pined: yearned intensely
irrevocably: unalterably

interminably: endlessly
knell: stroke or sound

sterile: germ-free or lifeless
sangfroid: self-possession

"Ever been to Fort Miami before?" he asked, guiding them through a **labyrinth** of white corridors.

"Every Internment Tuesday," Reth boasted.

"Good man," Truck said.

"Once," Jaden added quietly.

"You'll get the stomach for it in no time, Emory," Truck said, leading them into the bright Florida sun.

Jaden didn't have to see Reth's smirk in order to know it was there.

"The team will be running circuits about now. We can just catch the tail end if I skip the grand tour," Truck said. "Not much you'll need to know until you earn your way out of those gray uniforms. We just came from the admin building. Ripping Center is on your left." A low two-story building hunkered, clinging to the sand. "Mess hall's to the right and the barracks are behind that. For your first year you'll stay on base—passes on weekends. You'll have your own room, but it's nothing special."

"Just the basics, Sergeant, sir," Reth said. "That's all I need."

Jaden sighed. What a **sycophant**. With a new boss to brown-nose, Reth would be **insufferable**.

In front of him a quarter-mile track **delimited** an outdoor gymnasium. A squadron of black-clad soldiers worked out with everything from bars and beams to a full weight set.

"Fall in!" Truck shouted.

The squadron dropped into formation in front of them. At first glance they might be mistaken for younger clones of the sergeant. Same buzz-cuts, same solid, wide frames, same insanely bulging muscles. The ripper **motto**, "Strong bodies, strong minds," was obviously taken literally here.

Jaden searched the faces. Had some of these men been on the Raptor the night of his crash? The masks they had worn made it difficult to identify specific individuals, but the uniforms were the same.

---

labyrinth: maze   **insufferable:** unbearable   **motto:** saying
sycophant: flatterer   **delimited:** defined

How could he work with men who had seen him at his worst?

"At ease!" Truck shouted.

The squadron moved to parade rest.

Truck assumed a more casual tone. "Men, these are our new team members, Reth Warren and Jaden Emory."

"Another Warren, huh?" someone whispered.

"Yes, another Warren. I'm sure he'll do his family proud."

Jaden watched Reth puff up **haughtily** at the **compliment**.

"You'll be familiar with Recruit Emory as well, if not in name, in deed because—" Truck broke off with a cough.

Dammit! If they weren't the men who had rescued him, they'd know as much as they did once Truck told them.

Truck cleared his throat. "You'll know him because he's the man who pink-slipped the first raver found addicted to Joy."

A murmur of respect rolled through the ranks. Jaden knew that Joy had been new to him, but he didn't know Ally was the first addict to be caught while high on it.

A ripper with a black, triangular goatee and even blacker eyes stepped forward. "So he's the splitter responsible for that new policy?"

Truck laughed. "Actually, some lawmakers in D.C. are responsible for the policy."

Jaden had no idea what they were talking about. "Sergeant, sir," Jaden said, "what policy?"

"It hasn't been made public yet, but you're both rippers now, so I can tell you. All Joy-related addiction crimes are now punishable by double sentences, **retroactive** to that raver you turned in."

---

haughtily: proudly   **compliment:** words of praise   **retroactive:** extending back

Jaden fought to keep his emotions under control as he lay in bed, trying to lose himself in sleep. His upper bunk gave him a spectacular view of the barracks' ceiling two feet from his nose. The space where a bottom bunk might have been had been replaced by a small desk and chair. His footlocker had to fit in the closet. At least his **stark** surroundings allowed him privacy. It would be tough to keep a stiff upper lip sharing a room filled with **myriad** hardened pros. Nothing probably ever bothered any of the other rippers.

Of course, he was pretty convinced he was the only ripper who had ever taken Joy, too.

The dark, cold knot that Kim's splitting session had walled away had returned to his stomach, even heavier now. But there was a crack, a **crevice** in the surface, and for the last two nights as he lay in his **claustrophobic** bed, his mind uncluttered with the **rigors** of ripper training, his feelings for Ally would rush over him. And not so far behind were the tears that threatened to follow.

What had he done? Thanks to him, the girl he loved was either alligator bait or serving twenty years for her **proclivity** for dancing and listening to wild music.

But that wasn't her only problem. She was a Joy addict, and she deserved what she got.

But he had taken Joy, too. He was an addict, too—to his feelings for Ally. And therein lay the **quandary**. Didn't that put him on the wrong side of the force field?

He pounded his pillow with his fist. Dammit! There was no way he could **reconcile** his feelings. How could he **abjure** her and yet so **zealously** desire to be **exculpated** himself?

---

stark: harsh or bare
myriad: many
crevice: narrow opening
claustrophobic: narrowly enclosed
rigors: strict or cruel acts

proclivity: inclination or predisposition
quandary: perplexing situation
reconcile: bring together or account for

abjure: reject
zealously: fervently or passionately
exculpated: acquitted or absolved

When Jaden got his first day pass on Friday afternoon, there was only one thing on his mind—Joy. He couldn't stand the indecision, the warring **factions** inside of him. One minute he thought Ally deserved her sentence, and the next he was certain he should be sharing it. He needed a **reprieve** from his **anguish**. He needed peace, even just for a few hours.

He rented a low-end Gull 200 and cruised the edge of the U.Z., searching for the site of his crash and the stash he had buried. He narrowed the possibilities to a couple of spots. Anxious to be flying so near the force field after such a horrible crash, he landed the car beside a clump of bushes a bit further out and walked the remaining distance. The saw palmetto seemed to be in the right place, but if this was the actual site of his accident, the Ripper Squad had done a great job **eradicating** every sign of it.

He padded toward the fence. It sure looked a lot different from the ground. He didn't know what had been going through his head the other night. The **flimsy** wire fence only went up maybe fifty feet. He had been a fool to think this was the only thing keeping all those hardened criminals in the U.Z.

He threw a shell at the fence. It sparked and flew back at him in **shards**. If that was the way the fence reacted at a shell, walking away with his life was more than **fortuitous**.

Off in the distance, he noticed movement. Someone **rambled** toward him from the other side of the fence—several people, actually. Jaden jogged back to the car and ducked behind it.

"Right here's where it happened," a young boy's voice insisted. Jaden recognized the cocky swagger in the voice: Tail.

"Then how come there's no wreckage?" an older woman demanded.

"I saw it all," Tail said. "And the reason there's no crashed car is the best part of the story."

"So tell us already, Tail," an **emaciated** older man said.

Jaden peeked around the fender. The car was **obscured** by the

---

factions: groups or parties
reprieve: delay or relief
anguish: pain or anxiety
eradicating: exterminating

flimsy: weak or worthless
shards: fragments
fortuitous: fortunate or lucky

rambled: moved aimlessly
emaciated: very thin
obscured: concealed or hidden

bushes, but he could see well enough if he raised his head just a little. Tail stood with his back to the fence, looking just as scraggly in the daylight. Half a dozen **indigent** criminals clustered around him. They wore grubby, light-colored clothes with long sleeves and pants and ranged in age from a girl of maybe eight to an older man in his sixties.

"It'll cost you," Tail said.

Jaden smiled. He'd said those words countless times when he was just about the kid's age. When he was a dealer, he had **ascribed** a specific price for everything. **Commodifying** every aspect of his life was the only way he had survived on the streets, and it was obviously the way this boy survived. The only difference was that in the old days, The Corporation had taken pity on **juvenile** offenders. Didn't look like they had been as **lenient** with Tail.

A collective groan rose up from the crowd. "Not again," someone muttered.

"Not a full bar," Tail said with **alacrity**. "Just half-rations from each."

"I bet his story's not even worth it," the older woman said, spitting.

Tail turned away. "Well, if you don't think a rescue attempt is worth half-rations, then perhaps you're right. . . . " Jaden half-chuckled at the boy's **wily** grin. The kid knew what he was doing, all right.

"A rescue attempt?" the little girl asked. "Who was it? Who were they coming for?"

"Might be someone with a name a-begins with 'B' . . . " Tail said.

"Quarter-rations," the older man said.

"Deal," the sandy-haired kid said with a crooked grin.

Each member of the group handed Tail a square of something brown and sticky, which he wrapped in a crumpled piece of paper before shoving it in his pocket.

"Now everyone sit down and spread out. I want everyone to be able to see and hear."

---

indigent: very poor
ascribed: credited or assigned

commodifying: making commercial
juvenile: young or immature

lenient: indulgent
alacrity: cheerful readiness
wily: crafty

"Ain't nuttin' to see," a man grumbled.

"Shhh . . . " Tail said, his finger to his lips. He thrust his hands parallel to the ground, palms up, and then slowly brought them together over his head, bringing them back down until they pressed against his chest. "It begins!" he boomed. "At the darkest part of the night, the sky rained fire."

"Blaze?" the little girl cried. "Was it Blaze?"

"It was indeed. In a car as bright and shining as the stars, the color of the fire he will use to bring down the walls one day."

One of the women sighed **pensively**.

"Weren't no Blaze. Blaze is on the inside, like us," a man said.

"Gots a boat as can fly an' sail," a woman added. "In the Ten Thousand Islands."

"Blaze has powers both inside this world and outside of it," Tail said ominously. "Last night he completed the first test of his wall blaster, on this here very wall."

A soft murmur rose from the group, and they looked at the plain wire fence with a newfound awe and respect.

"Then how come the wall's still standing?" a woman asked.

"I told you, that's the best part. Minutes after the device **detonated**, the place was swarming with Outs."

"Perims?" the older man asked.

"Blue suits and black coats. Scooped it all away. Even fixed the trees and the grass."

"Why would they do that?"

"They wanted Blaze's device," Tail said, "but he was too smart for them. The big boom-crash was because it had a self-destruct. Nothing blows up like that on its own."

The crowd nodded sagely in agreement.

"What about Blaze?" one of the women asked.

"He got away of course. As soon as the device did its job, he hightailed it out of there."

---

pensively: thoughtfully   **detonated:** blew up

"So why isn't the fence still down?" the older man asked.

"The black coats fixed it. Put it all back the way it was."

"An' how come you're still here to tell us about it? How come you didn't hightail it out of there right behind Blaze?"

"Didn't know at first that the wall was down. By the time I figured it out, the blue suits and black coats had shown up. I wouldn't have made it far with them snooping around."

"So what's Blaze going to do next?" the woman asked.

"He doesn't know," the older man said. "He's just a kid."

"I may be just a kid, but I'd know what I'd do if I were him," Tail said. "I'd take my data from the explosion back to the lab and start building me an even bigger boom-crash. Take out a big enough chunk of the wall and the perims and blue suits won't be able to fix it before a whole bunch of Ins become Outs."

"Hooray!" the little girl cried.

"I knew it," the older man said. "Just like I thought."

"Blaze will be coming for all of us soon," a woman agreed. "Let's go back and tell the others the good news!"

"Hey!" Tail cried. "It's my story!"

"Not any more," the older man said, winking. "We paid for it and now it's ours."

The crowd bustled off the way they had come, eager to pass along Tail's story.

Tail threw a rock hard at the wall and it sparked into **shrapnel**.

As the group faded in the distance, Jaden stood up and called to Tail. "Hey, kid!"

When Tail turned to see who had called to him, he froze. His gaze didn't lock on Jaden's, but rather on the side of his head.

Dammit! Why did people have to stare at his plate?

"It doesn't hurt, if that's what you're worried about," Jaden said.

Mesmerized by the gleaming golden plate, Tail eyed it instead of him as he backed away from the force field. "You never told

---

shrapnel: fragments of a projectile

me you were a ripper."

"Trainee," Jaden said, plucking at his gray uniform.

Tail teased a few more steps back.

"What's wrong?"

"Can you read my mind through the force field?"

Jaden laughed. "I can't read anyone's mind, force field or not."

"You're lying. That's what rippers do."

Jaden shook his head in **dissent**. "No, it's not, and even if it was, I'm just a **novice**. I can't do much of anything yet."

"The signs say rippers read minds and fix them."

"What signs?"

"They're all over in here. They say if you get your mind Ripped, you get out."

"Well, that much is true, but I'm not **clairvoyant**. I can connect to an addict's mind and smooth away the problems, but only under the proper conditions."

"The proper conditions don't include seeing a likely candidate, do they? I'd like my brain to stay just the way it is, thank you very much."

Jaden laughed. "Just come back already. I want to ask you about your **apocryphal** story."

"What about it?" Tail said, approaching the fence once more.

"What were you telling those folks? You twisted everything around until there wasn't a single grain of truth in there."

"The group, they want to hear about their hero Blaze, not some high fancy crashin' his sports car. Gives *them* hope and *me* a **modicum** of food in my belly. I figure it's an even trade."

"So is Blaze a real person?"

Tail shrugged. "As long as I keep spinning stories about him, he will be. And as long as I keep getting fed doing it, I'll keep weaving my tales." He **surreptitiously foraged** in his pocket for a scrap of ration bar. "Come back for your pill?" the **perspicacious** kid asked.

---

dissent: difference of opinion
novice: beginner
clairvoyant: seeing beyond what is ordinarily seen

apocryphal: fictional
modicum: small portion
surreptitiously: secretly

foraged: looked for food
perspicacious: shrewd or clear thinking

"How'd you know?"

"You were kind of obvious that night. I'd be surprised if the blue suits didn't find 'em. They went over everything pretty good."

"I haven't checked yet. I wasn't sure I was in the right place."

Tail laughed. "You're such an Out! Couldn't find your way if they popped out your brain and replaced it with a global positioning system, could you?"

Jaden started to kick up dirt around the palm with the heel of his shoe. He hadn't buried the pill very deep. It should turn up with a couple of scrapes.

After ten minutes of **excavating** with his shoe followed by twenty minutes of digging on his hands and knees, Jaden finally gave up the search. His fingers throbbed, and his nails had split. He wiped the sweat from his forehead and left it moist and gritty.

"Figured the blue suits found it," Tail said **sanctimoniously**. "What do you need pills for anyhow? You're on the outside."

"That pill will help me find the girl I lost," Jaden said, and in a way it was true. Joy would help him be with Ally, and at peace, one more time.

"If she's inside, you're not going to find her from out there."

Jaden looked down at the sandspur-covered pants of his gray uniform and the caked sand beneath his broken nails. Like the night of the crash, the kid spoke the truth. He'd have to get inside if he wanted to find out what happened to Ally.

"Do you think you might be able to find out what happened to her?" Jaden asked.

Tail shrugged. "For a price, maybe. But what you really need is a runner."

"A runner?"

"They can get stuff in and out of the U.Z."

"Where would I find one?"

"Dunno. You got a dealer, right? Ask him."

---

excavating: digging out   **sanctimoniously:** in a falsely holy way

*   *   *   *   *

Jaden pointed the clunky Gull 200 toward Tamlando. With luck on his side for a change, he found the dealer he was seeking at his Ybor Mall food court haunt.

Unfortunately Squeeze saw Jaden, too, and took off in the opposite direction.

Jaden followed him. "Squeeze! Wait!" What was with people running from him today?

"Roar, roar, and out the door, splitter. My customers don't like loud lions on the prowl."

Jaden lowered his voice. "I'm sorry, but I need your help."

Squeeze continued walking **briskly** toward the parking garage, and Jaden trotted after him.

"Saying you need help is like saying peanut butter needs chocolate. You're just not Amsterdam if you're not in need of help."

Jaden sighed, exasperated. He still hated the sound of that nickname. Even with everything that was happening, he liked to think he was a long way from the useless punk that name had referred to. "Look, this is different."

"Different from finding your girl, getting you high, and keeping your butt from getting kicked at the warehouse? I've helped plenty. And all I ever wanted was a gold star and maybe a milk carton that wasn't recyclable. Is that too much to ask?"

Squeeze's **non sequitur stupefied** Jaden. He had never been sure of everything Squeeze was talking about, but he did know there were certain things the dealer was always good for. Once Squeeze heard him out, Jaden knew he'd offer his assistance. He just had to charge ahead. "I need you to get me into the U.Z."

Squeeze snorted. "In's not a problem. Tell any Senior Manager how you've been occupying your time and you'll get *in*." He continued toward the parking garage, but his pace had slowed. "I do say

---

briskly: energetically   **non sequitur:** illogical response   **stupefied:** astonished

out's a sight tougher, though."

"That's not what I mean."

"It'd work. You could find your girl and have a real Florida crack-er wedding. A possum as best man, a raccoon as maid of honor. Just think of how cute it would be if you gave them tiny hats to wear. . . ." His voice trailed off.

"Squeeze—"

"Of course that's assuming she's not dead already."

"Nice. Look, it's clear you're not the right person to deal with. Ice cream bar woman looked like a **sovereign** Susie, if you know what I mean, a real take-charge kind of woman." Jaden knew how to hit Squeeze's vulnerable spot. No street boss liked to be told some-one else was better than he was. "I'll just drop by the warehouse on my way home. . . . "

Now *that* made Squeeze stop. "You're already running with the top dog, but the question is, are you willing to play fetch?"

"Huh?"

Squeeze pushed his hat back and wiped his forehead, surveying Jaden. "When I throw my Frisbee, my dogs come back with it, ya understand?"

"No."

Squeeze rolled his eyes and sighed. His tone and demeanor changed. He sounded like a Corporation voice-over artist from the Midwest. "I can get you in, but you can't stay, and you can't bring your raver out. Along with smuggling yourself in, you'll be smug-gling in a few items of my choosing as well."

Jaden's stomach turned. "That's kind of risky, don't you think? I could get nailed just walking around with the stuff before I even made it across the wall." Jaden cringed at the thought of being a prisoner himself.

Squeeze resorted to baby talk. "Awww . . . did the big bad **maver-ick** get an itty bitty day job and forget to work the night shift once in

---

sovereign: ruler   **maverick:** independent
                                     person

a while to stay in practice?"

Though he didn't want to admit it, there was a sliver of truth to Squeeze's **insinuation**. Jaden *had* been out of the game for quite some time. And it wasn't as if he was going to start out in the minors. Breaking into the U.Z. was the championship game.

But the whole reason he had gotten back into this mess initially was because Ally needed him. And she still needed him. He couldn't leave her behind that fence, not knowing what had happened to her. He couldn't **endure** another night reliving the heartless, **sadistic** things he had said and done to her. He had more **virtue** than that. And it was time he started showing it.

"I'll do it."

*   *   *   *   *

As the **nascent** moon rose, Jaden's speedboat coughed through the warm waters of the Gulf of Mexico. His wet suit already itched, and he wished he had waited until he arrived before putting it on and **embedding** the contraband in the liner. He just didn't want to spend any more time hovering outside the U.Z. force field than he had to.

The homing **medallion** Squeeze gave him blinked its directions at him, and he piloted the boat accordingly. He wore the device on a cord around his neck like a stopwatch, correcting his course each time the medallion blinked a change. About an hour after he had taken off, the medallion glowed solid red. He dropped anchor.

The wake **cleaved** the surface of the Gulf, rippling back at him as it hit the invisible force field. No fence way out in the middle of the Gulf of Mexico, just the wall. The hole he sought would be at the bottom of the ocean. Squeeze had paid some **disgruntled** force field monitor a fortune to create it. With his wet suit and breathing equipment, he'd be able to swim through the hole with his contra-

insinuation: suggestion	**virtue:** admirable quality	**medallion:** large medal
endure: withstand	**nascent:** coming into being	**cleaved:** split
sadistic: excessively cruel	**embedding:** enclosing	**disgruntled:** dissatisfied

band, but nobody on the other side would be able to dive deep enough to get through. Even if they could, they'd need the homing device to find the hole. You couldn't just swim around and feel your way through. Just like the force field on land, even the most casual brush could fry you.

Jaden tested his breathing equipment. The pacifier-shaped device fit comfortably in his mouth, and the compressed air in the quarter-sized pockets on either side tasted a bit stale, but it would do. Jaden slipped on his fins over his sneakers and sat on the edge of the boat, shining his waterproof headlamp into the dark water. Would there be sharks? Alligators? He'd even heard rumors of crocodiles. In the waters around the Ten Thousand Islands, the freshwater rivers and streams poured into the salt water of the Gulf of Mexico creating a marshy **estuary**. Sharks and crocs preferred salt water and alligators preferred fresh, but bottom line was that he could find one or all of them beneath him.

Well, there was no point in overthinking it now. He'd find out whatever was waiting for him soon enough. Jaden secured his motorized personal **propulsion gauntlets** on his wrists. Combined with the flippers he wore, his P.P.G.s would not only help him navigate quickly through the hole in the U.Z., but they'd also serve as his transportation on the other side. All he had to do was extend his hands in front of him like a superhero soaring off to save the girl, and his P.P.G.s would do the rest.

Jaden plunged into the warm waters and aimed his personal propulsion gauntlets toward the ocean floor. The bulging pockets of contraband made him overly **buoyant**, and it was tough to swim at first, but he adjusted. His roaming headlamp beam lit mostly on **nondescript** muddy-colored fish with long, **lateral** stripes, maybe snook? Once in a while he'd catch a long flash of silver when a tarpon checked him out, but none of the more worrisome predators.

He switched the homing medallion from the long-range setting

---

estuary: where a tide meets a river current
propulsion: something causing forward motion

gauntlets: armored gloves
buoyant: able to float

nondescript: dull
lateral: extending from side to side

to short-range and the glow turned from solid red to pulsing neon green. The distance indicators assured him he was on course, but he swam as straight as possible. He couldn't afford to even graze the force field. When the homing medallion glowed a solid green, he crossed his fingers and dove through the force field into the uncharted lands of the Unemployed Zone.

When the homing medallion indicated he had cleared the force field, Jaden swam another thirty feet along the bottom of the ocean, just to make sure, before beginning his **ascent**.

He surfaced in a dark, unfamiliar world.

Expecting the water to smell as salty as it tasted, Jaden was surprised by the fresh, moist air that greeted him. He punched the coordinates to his contact's **lair** into the homing medallion and headed southwest through one of the shallow **tributaries**. In most places the water was no more than five feet deep now. To either side of him the twisted mangrove roots of the islands clutched like witches' knuckles ready to snatch him away.

He wove back in toward the center of the channel.

Off in the distance he heard the roar of an engine. He had no intention of sticking around to find out what it was attached to. He balled his fists to make his P.P.G.s **accelerate** and kept his head down to minimize the glow from his headlamp.

The engine roar grew louder and Jaden could tell there were several of the machines in the area. A voice hallooed, closer than Jaden would have expected. Several lights bobbed in the darkness, charting a path parallel to his.

An engine roared behind him, creating a wake that threatened to knock Jaden off course.

Another machine tore past him, and another, each coming closer than the one before. Within seconds Jaden found himself encircled by a fleet of **pernicious** pirates with boats unlike any he had ever seen.

Their **antediluvian** airboats consisted of **multifarious antiquated**

---

ascent: rising up
lair: refuge or hiding place
tributaries: streams feeding into larger streams or lakes
accelerate: speed up
pernicious: very harmful
antediluvian: old and outdated
multifarious: diverse
antiquated: old or out of style

car parts and carved cypress propellers **cobbled** together with battered tin hulls. Dozens of crews of threes and fours jeered at Jaden. The fiery reflections of torches dotted the water all around him.

Someone gave a sharp whistle, and the fleet coasted simultaneously to a halt. A gruff pirate with shoulder-length black curls maneuvered his airboat within fifteen feet of him. "Get your butt on the boat, Runner," he said.

One of the two other pirates in the boat with him cast a rope in the water.

Jaden froze, not making a move toward the rope. He was sure if he took hold of that rope the **scurrilous** pirates would slit his throat, steal his breathing gear, and make for land with his contraband. As **indifferent** as he was about the last one, neither of the first two was acceptable.

He could dive back down and stay under until they left, but Squeeze had been quite clear that his breathing gear would only get him down to the bottom and back up twice, no more. If he dove to escape, he'd never be able to get back out.

"Stop stalling, Runner. We ain't got all night. Don doesn't like to be kept waiting."

Jaden found his voice. "Don didn't send you. Nobody knew I was coming."

A **raucous** cackle rose from the crew.

"Just get on the boat before I have to send some of my boys down for you," the curly-haired pirate said.

Jaden hesitated, but realized he didn't really have a choice, so he took hold of the rope and let himself be hauled aboard. The airboat rocked as he settled into his chair.

"Hand over the **booty**," Curly said.

"My instructions are to give it directly to Don."

"We's Don's men," Curly said with a **cunning** grin. "We'll take it

---

cobbled: put together hastily
scurrilous: evil or abusive

indifferent: unconcerned
raucous: rowdy or unpleasantly loud

booty: plunder or prize
cunning: crafty

to him for you and you can hop right on back in the water and paddle home."

Unflappable, Jaden willed his voice to stay firm. "Only to Don." It wasn't just that his instructions from Squeeze had been very specific on the point, but in order to find out anything at all about Ally he needed to talk to the man in charge.

"Suit yourself. Just thought such a fine fancy as yourself would rather be off playing Groundhog's Day at the club instead of **gallivanting** through the swamp." Curly gave another screeching two-fingered whistle and the **posse** roared to life.

The mangrove clusters of the Ten Thousand Islands streaked past. The islands varied in size from miles across to only a few feet. Almost every one had a posted sign that read *Rip & Release*. He thought about Tail's frightened reaction to his ripping cybernetics and was thankful that the hood of his wetsuit **concealed** his implants. If the prisoners really did think that rippers could read minds like Tail said, he wouldn't be a very popular guy. It was better to literally keep it under wraps for the time being.

They zipped on for over an hour, finally docking on a marshy strip of land.

"Take this," Curly said, tossing Jaden what looked like a walking stick. One end had been sharpened to a point.

"I'm fine," Jaden said. "I'm in good shape."

"Won't stay that way without that stick," Curly said **cryptically**, "but suit yourself."

Jaden took the stick.

Half the **eclectic** crew stayed with the boats, and the other half, about twenty men, formed a single-file line for the trek through the swamp. Jaden assumed a spot near the end. As the foliage drew in around them, mosquitoes and a host of other insects swarmed around him. His wet suit protected his **torso** as well as his upper arms and legs, but his half-suit left lots of tender flesh exposed.

---

unflappable: assured and showing self-control
gallivanting: roaming about for pleasure

posse: group or entourage
concealed: hid
cryptically: mysteriously

eclectic: made up of various elements
torso: the human trunk

He swatted constantly, much to the great humor of the **resilient** pirates, who didn't seemed bothered at all by the bugs. He couldn't tell if they simply ignored them or wore some sort of defense.

Within minutes, the **tortuous** path had them wading thigh-deep through dark water. At first Jaden tried to keep track of each twist and turn, but his attempts were futile. He was lost in the Everglades.

A **hardy** pirate with a scraggly beard that reeked of kerosene dropped into step next to him. "The gators will mostly leave you alone if you leave them alone," he said. "Just don't startle one. They likes to see you first."

Whether first or last, Jaden had an **aversion** to the idea of an alligator seeing him at all.

"And watch out for the ones with scars," the pirate continued. "They're smart and **ornery**."

"And really nasty," another pirate said, overcoming them from behind. As he passed, Jaden saw that half his upper lip had been sliced away. Jaden shuddered.

"They must be taking the night off, huh?" Jaden asked. "I haven't seen a single one."

More mean-spirited laughter echoed through the **primeval** swamp.

When the laughter **subsided**, the pirate pointed off to the left. "There's one."

Jaden peered into the **protean** darkness. "I don't see anything."

"Bubbles," the **judicious** pirate said, pointing at a small stream of bubbles barely breaking the surface. "Stay away from the bubbles." He shifted to the right and Jaden quickly followed.

"You mean there's an alligator underneath the water right now?"

Again, **gales** of laughter whipped through the **brigands**.

"Naw," the pirate said.

---

resilient: recovering easily
tortuous: winding or crooked
hardy: bold or robust
aversion: dislike
ornery: bad tempered

primeval: ancient or primitive
subsided: settled or lessened
protean: able to assume different forms

judicious: wise
gales: emotional outbursts
brigands: bandits

"I'm glad of that."

"Could be a crocodile."

Jaden was glad to set foot on dry land again—well, mostly dry land. Despite the mosquitoes, alligators, and crocodiles, he knew each step he took in this poisonous land brought him closer to Ally.

His gaze darted to a rustling motion on the **periphery** of the trail.

A black, four-foot-long snake slithered across the path in front of Jaden. When it saw him, it coiled and reared back, hissing.

"Where's your stick?" the pirate behind him asked. "Use your stick!"

Jaden threw his stick at the snake and missed by three feet. The thick snake struck at the movement before **orienting** back on Jaden.

The pirate pushed him aside and hefted his own stick like a javelin. The snake pressed its head further back into its body, preparing to strike. It opened its jaws wider than the **span** of Jaden's hand, revealing a puffy white inside and two very deadly fangs.

The pirate jammed the stick down the snake's throat, pinning it.

The pirate walked past Jaden, scooping up the stick Jaden had dropped.

"Aren't you going to kill it?" Jaden asked.

"You can, if you want. Probably better to spend your time getting a new stick."

Jaden followed the pirate's advice.

After passing through several guard checkpoints over the next hour, they arrived at a **massive compound**. Dozens of **rudimentary** huts on stilts formed the perimeter, their roofs thatched with palm fronds. Instead of stairs, ladders led up to most; those without had probably already pulled them up for the night. He wondered if the stilts were a defense from the water, the wild animals, or the other criminals.

---

periphery: boundary
orienting: directing toward

span: distance between thumb and little finger
massive: large

compound: walled-in group of buildings
rudimentary: primitive

In the center a bonfire raged. Two longer buildings opposed each other in the circle. The basic rectangle of one reminded Jaden of the barracks back in Fort Miami. The other was a more **elaborate** two-story building on stilts. No ladders this time, but real stairs leading to the second floor.

Curly shepherded him up the stairs. An airy balcony opened up into a large meeting hall. Smudge fires smoldered in cauldrons along the walls giving off smoke that kept the bugs at bay. Lanterns hung from posts down the center, leading the way to a **dais** where a dark figure sat on an oversized chair. He leaned forward at their entry, and the fire cast flickering shadows on him. He wore black jeans and a black turtleneck, despite the heat. His face was a lumpy oval, and his bald head gleamed in the firelight. His ears were misshapen, and a gold hoop swung from one ear. He wore black sunglasses, even thought it was night. Jaden couldn't see the eyes behind the sunglasses, but somehow the man's gaze still chilled him.

"Don, we picked up the runner," Curly said.

"Dammit, Mitch! I told you to use my pirate name. It's Gaspar, José Gaspar!" he shouted.

"Sure, Don, sure . . . " Mitch nodded, his dark curls shaking. He sauntered over to the cluster of rough-looking men apparently playing dice on the floor.

"Gaspar!" Don bellowed.

A scantily clad girl who was reclining at Don's feet cringed, like a cocker spaniel puppy with a rolled-up newspaper being held over its head. Mitch might get away with being **impudent**, but not all of Don's **minions** were eager to hear him raise his voice.

"What have you got for me, Runner?"

Jaden unzipped the top of his wetsuit and pulled out the collection of sealed packages. "Squeeze sent these for you, Gaspar. I don't know what's in them." Jaden could guess, though. Probably drugs, alcohol, cigarettes—maybe even an MP3 player or two. The low,

---

elaborate: complex
dais: raised platform

impudent: insolent or disrespectful

minions: followers or underlings

flat packages were well-cushioned, so it could be anything. Maybe even Joy, not that the addicts inside the U.Z. needed it.

"At least somebody gets it right," Gaspar said. He leaned in toward Jaden conspiratorially. "I mean, how tough is it to use a man's name?"

"Not tough at all, Gaspar, sir."

Gaspar clucked his tongue. "Too much."

"Okay." Jaden began to zip his wetsuit back up.

"Hold on." Gaspar snapped his fingers at one of the girls lounging nearby. A **voluptuous** brunette wiggled over to a table, picked up a bunch of similar packages, handed them to Jaden, and wiggled back toward Gaspar.

"Take those to Squeeze," the pirate said, more interested in watching the brunette's wiggle than talking to Jaden.

"He didn't say anything about bringing stuff back."

"It's what runners do, kid."

Jaden couldn't imagine what Unemployed addicts inside might have that employees outside would want, but he had no intention of being **truculent**. "No problem, then. I'll just load up and be on my way." Jaden unzipped his suit again. "One thing, though. I hear you're a man in the know. I'm trying to find a girl."

"Well, we've got plenty of those around here!" Gaspar guffawed, wrapping his arm around the **submissive** brunette he had been ogling and pulling her onto his lap.

Jaden ignored the **lascivious** comment. "Her name's Ally Fayre. She's a raver. Just interred last Tuesday." Jaden described her.

"Don't know her, but someone else might. We've got quite a few ravers in the compound."

The dice-playing pirates snickered. Jaden had **surmised** that Gaspar's harem was made up mostly of captured ravers.

"Lanna!" Gaspar bellowed.

A **lanky** girl with blonde hair down to her butt skittered over **compliantly**. "Yes, Don?"

---

voluptuous: having a sensual form
truculent: cruel or prone to fighting

submissive: surrendering to others
lascivious: lewd or lustful

surmised: guessed
lanky: ungracefully tall and thin
compliantly: submissively

"Dammit, it's Gaspar!" He pushed the brunette off his lap.

Lanna flinched. "Sorry, Gaspar. I just forgot."

"Let's see if you can remember this, then." He turned to Jaden. "Tell her about your **wench**."

Jaden repeated his description.

"Never heard of her, Do—Gaspar." She turned to go back to the cluster of gambling pirates in the corner.

Gaspar grabbed her long blond hair and yanked her backward. "Think again, you stupid **git**!"

The girl's eyes widened. "I really haven't heard of her. There are lots of ravers, lots of girls." Lanna tried to adopt a **seductive** tone, but her **frantic** fear leaked through. "Not all of them are as lucky as I was to get picked up and brought here to please you. Most get murdered and dumped in the first few days. I swear I've never heard of her, Don."

Gaspar bristled and his eyebrows crushed into one. He seethed deeper and deeper shades of red until it looked like his bald head might pop off at the neck from the pressure.

"It's Gaspar, dammit!" he bellowed. He grabbed Lanna's long blonde hair, wrapped it around her throat and yanked.

Lanna gasped out one last breath of surprise and choked, clawing at the rope of her own hair around her neck.

---

wench: young woman
git: foolish or worthless person

seductive: alluring or tempting

frantic: nervous and emotional

Lanna coughed and struggled, her face turning red. Gaspar kicked her feet out from under her and slid to the floor with a *whomp*, her throat bearing the weight of the rest of her body.

Jaden didn't know what to do. He couldn't just stand by and watch Gaspar kill the girl, but even if he could do something to stop Gaspar, he'd never make it out alive. He'd never be able to **evade** a camp full of pirates. He shifted from one foot to the other, clenching his fists at his sides.

Lanna's face flushed deep red, almost purple as her arms and legs **flailed** in the air in a final desperate attempt to free herself.

Gaspar's **maniacal** grin remained as he continued to choke her, as if the man were actually enjoying committing murder.

Jaden felt fury course through him. He took a step forward to help Lanna, but immediately a strong hand clasped his shoulder and pulled him back.

Mitch whispered in his ear, "A raver's not worth getting killed over, Runner. Don't make me have to bury two people tonight."

Jaden shook him off. "Gaspar!" His voice rang out, silencing the pirates as they turned to look at him.

Gaspar paused, regarding Jaden, his breathing heavy. "You have something to say, kid?" He fixed his gaze on Jaden as if he were planning to throttle him next.

"I almost forgot—I have something else for you."

Gaspar relaxed his hold on Lanna, forgetting her for the moment, and stalked up to Jaden. Lanna fell to her knees, retching and gasping for air.

"Runner, I don't like being toyed with. If you've got a package,

---

evade: dodge   **flailed:** swung or beat   **maniacal:** insane or frantic

cough it up. Now."

Jaden regarded Gaspar through his mop of dreds. "It's not a package, Gaspar. It's a message."

"A message? What message?"

"A message from Squeeze. For your ears only." Jaden beckoned **conspiratorily**, and Gaspar leaned forward so Jaden could speak it into his ear. "Squeeze says that Chicken Little was right." Nonsense words invented to sound **portentous** and **encrypted**.

"Squeeze said that?"

Jaden nodded. Apparently, against all odds, the words had struck a chord with Gaspar.

Gaspar nodded thoughtfully, sunk in a **reverie**. Momentarily, he shook it off, looking up. "That kid's here, right?" Gaspar asked Mitch.

"I'll go get him."

Jaden felt his pulse start to race. He really wanted to get news about Ally, but after what he had just witnessed, his primary goal was to escape this violently **mercurial** character as soon as possible. Now what was he going to have to watch?

Mitch returned with a wiry eleven-year-old with a loping **gait**—Tail.

Tail didn't look to either side as he **sidled** forward. "Evening, Gaspar," Tail said. "What can I do for you?"

"This runner is looking for some raver wench." Gaspar's bored tone made it clear his hospitality was **ebbing**.

Tail turned and faced Jaden. "Figured you'd show up here eventually, Jaden," Tail said. "Everyone does. Gaspar's the man with the juice."

Gaspar seemed to perk up at the sincere and legitimate flattery.

"Do you know something then, about Ally?" Jaden asked.

"Checked with the ravers along the northern border. She's not with them, but a small band just recently set off for Ibiza."

The now-familiar cackle of the pirates was punctuated with the giggles of Gaspar's **harem**.

---

conspiratorily: suggestive of a conspiracy
portentous: solemn or foreshadowing
encrypted: encoded

reverie: daydream
mercurial: unpredictable
gait: way of walking
sidled: moved furtively

ebbing: receding or lessening
harem: group of women associated with one man

"There is no such place!" Mitch said.

"The ravers think there is," Tail said. "They're searching the Ten Thousand Islands."

"What's *Ibiza*?" Jaden asked. He'd never known what the rave password had meant, even when he used it to get in to the tanker.

"It's the mythical island haven of the ravers," Tail said. "Their **utopia**."

Murmurs rose from the darkness as several of the girls around Gaspar spoke in hushed, **reverent** tones.

"Ibiza means peace . . . Ibiza means love . . . Ibiza means unity . . . Ibiza means respect . . . "

Gaspar threw his hands up in the air. "And Ibiza means death if you're stupid enough to go looking for it!"

"He's right," Tail said. "Ravers aren't hardened survivalists like Gaspar and his crew. There aren't many supply distribution points in the Ten Thousand Islands. They'll be lost and hungry in a matter of days. If the gators don't get them, the cottonmouths will."

"Or the pirates," Mitch said.

Cheers of cocky agreement arose from the men.

"Write her off as dead!" Gaspar bellowed.

"Even if you found her, you couldn't keep her safe," Tail said. "The only sure way would be to take her and leave. It can't be done. No one has ever escaped the Unemployed Zone. If they had, I'd know."

"The kid knows everyone's story," Gaspar said.

"I'd better. It's why you let me hang out here from time to time, isn't it?"

"Well, it's not for yer pretty face," Gaspar said, his **demeaning** laugh harsh. Tail took no notice of it.

"I can't give up on Ally, not until I know for sure what happened to her," Jaden protested.

"Your funeral," Gaspar said.

---

utopia: ideal place **reverent:** worshipful **demeaning:** lowering in status

Jaden knew he'd better take the opening to leave while Gaspar was still in a **benevolent** mood. "I think I'm all packed up," he said, patting his full wetsuit. "Is there anything else you need from me, Gaspar, or do I have your permission to leave?"

"You can leave if you want, but my crew ain't heading out until morning."

"I really need to get back to my boat tonight," Jaden said. "I can't have a patrol picking it up."

"Good luck with that," Mitch said, laughing.

Jaden knew he'd never make it back on his own. He'd barely avoided countless **deleterious** snakes and alligators when he had someone to **abet** him. How could he do it alone?

"It's time I get moving again, too," Tail said. "I'll guide him back—for a price, of course."

The pirates guffawed and Jaden couldn't **suppress** a grin. "I'm **amenable**. Take me to my boat and we'll discuss **remuneration** on the trail."

*   *   *   *   *

The two **sojourners** traveled in silence until they cleared all the checkpoints and verified they hadn't been followed.

"Thanks," Jaden said.

"I didn't want to be around when the next idiot called Gaspar Don again."

Jaden laughed. "He just doesn't look like a Gaspar."

"It's new for him. Tough name to match his **infamy**. Meanest pirate warlord in the U.Z. Nobody messes with Don."

"You mean *Gaspar*," Jaden corrected, and they both laughed. The bugs still gnawed on every inch of exposed flesh, and alligators still prowled the dark waters, but shared laughter made the trip a bit more tolerable. "So there are others like Don?"

---

benevolent: generous and kind
deleterious: harmful
abet: encourage or incite

suppress: subdue
amenable: willing or obedient
remuneration: payment

sojourners: persons staying temporarily
infamy: disgrace

"Oh, hundreds. Each section of land, each island—practically each cabbage palm—has its own pirate warlord. Most warlords pick crews with addictions that **correspond** to their own. The warlords in the Keys pretty much keep to themselves. Specialty islands with more civilized criminals.

"The warlords in the Ten Thousand Islands are a bit rougher. Mostly drunks trying to hide stills and pirates trying to find them so they can use the alcohol to fuel their airboats.

"The ravers don't have a warlord of their own. Without protection, they pretty much just cluster near the northern boundary and wait to get picked off.

"Don took over the land nobody else wanted, and takes the baddest of the bad into his crew. Doesn't matter what they're into. He'll raid anyone who's got it and get it for his men." Tail paused to stake another hissing cottonmouth.

"So if they're such **ruffians**, why do you hang around with them?"

"Maybe I'm a ruffian too. Maybe I only offered to take you back to your boat so I could kill you and steal the packages you're taking back."

Jaden's breath caught in his throat. Had the **precocious** kid **beguiled** him? Was he going to die here in this **heinous** swamp?

"Or maybe I'm *eleven*, Jaden, and I need to keep on people's good sides."

Jaden forced himself to relax. The whole **escapade** had **overtaxed** his imagination. "But you told me you didn't work for any one pirate."

"I don't. I work for them all, and I'm sick of it. I'm tired of moving around all the time so I don't **inadvertently** annoy anyone."

They had reached the bay, and Tail uncovered a flat-bottomed **skiff** hidden in the bushes down the bank from Gaspar's airboats. They set it in the water and used two long poles to steer away from

---

correspond: are equivalent to or parallel
ruffians: bullies
precocious: unusually mature

beguiled: attracted through deceit
heinous: shockingly bad
escapade: adventure

overtaxed: demanded too much of
inadvertently: without meaning to
skiff: small boat

the Everglades and into the Ten Thousand Islands estuary. The shallow waters never measured more than five or six feet, and although Jaden figured he'd have made better time with his motorized personal propulsion gauntlets, he appreciated the ability to stay dry.

"Glad not to be swimming?" Tail asked.

"Oh, yeah," Jaden said. "I'm lucky. If you hadn't been at Don's, I'd be boatless right now."

"It's not a **coincidence** that I was at Don's when you arrived."

"Oh, no?"

"I can read more than these **pithy** *Rip and Release* signs. I can read runner code."

"There's a runner code? Go figure."

"Yeah. It's a series of light-based **semaphores** that Ins and Outs exchange. If you know where to look, and you spend a little time code-breaking, you can figure out when people are coming and from where."

"That must be how Don's crew knew where to find me." Jaden's arms already ached from pushing the boat through the mangrove islands. "Seems like something my boss could have told me."

They lapsed into silence until they reached the **impregnable** force field. The ripples from the skiff echoed off the invisible wall.

"Guess this is it," Jaden said, checking his equipment. "Thanks again, for every—"

"Take me with you!" Tail blurted.

"Oh, kid, I'd like to, but I can't."

Tail's eyes darkened. "You mean you won't."

"I mean I *can't*. They only provided enough air for one person to get back under the force field." Jaden immediately regretted his **revelation**. Miles away from any assistance, all Tail would have to do to take his equipment was pull a knife, or even push him overboard.

"I'm a good swimmer," Tail insisted. "I could follow you."

Jaden relaxed. Horrible thoughts shouldn't pop first to his

---

coincidence: connected events happening at once by chance
pithy: concise

semaphores: systems for signaling
impregnable: unconquerable or impenetrable

revelation: surprise

mind. Tail was just a kid, after all. Unfortunately he was a kid who reminded Jaden far too much of himself at that age. If Tail was one-tenth as devious as Jaden had been, he was right to worry. "It's too deep."

"Let me at least try."

"I can't. No escapees allowed, or the guard who opens the force field won't do it anymore."

"I can't stay here, Jaden. It's only a matter of time before I stop being the cute kid. Please, let me go with you." Tail's eyes **glistened** with tears.

Jaden had to look away. "I'm really sorry. I'd take you if I could." He knew the words didn't really help Tail as much as he meant them.

"Yeah." Tail gazed into the dark water.

"Really, I would." Jaden put his hand on Tail's shoulder.

Tail backed away. "You still gotta pay me," he groused.

Jaden frowned. "I really don't have anything with me I can give you," he said, slipping his flippers on over his shoes.

"Those." Tail pointed at his feet.

"I can't dive deep enough fast enough without them."

"Not the flippers, the shoes."

"You want my shoes?"

"Yes."

Jaden shrugged and took off his shoes, handing them to Tail. If the kid **coveted** them, he could have them. His flippers would be a bit loose, but he'd manage.

"I'm really sorry again, Tail," Jaden said with **empathy** in his voice. "I've gotta go."

Jaden put the breathing device into his mouth and jumped into the cold, dark water. He adjusted the coordinates on his homing device and then activated his personal propulsion gauntlets.

Seconds later he heard a splash from above. He turned his head-

---

glistened: glittered or sparkled

coveted: desired enviously

empathy: understanding and sensitivity

lamp upward and saw Tail swimming toward him.

Dumb, **impetuous** *kid,* Jaden thought. Tail couldn't hold his breath that long. Jaden would just keep swimming and when the kid ran out of air, he'd turn back.

But Tail didn't. Without flippers and the benefit of his P.P.G., Tail swam slower than Jaden, but he didn't give up. If he didn't **abort** and turn back soon, Tail wouldn't have enough air to reach the surface.

Jaden gazed over his shoulder. A five-foot-long black tip shark prowled between Jaden and Tail. The shock of seeing the large blue-gray predator ripped the last few bubbles of air from Tail's lungs, and he pumped quickly toward the safety of the surface.

*　　*　　*　　*　　*

The night sky lightened in preparation for a muggy dawn, and Squeeze's purple derby created a domed profile as he paced on the dock, waiting for Jaden to tie up the boat. As anxious as Squeeze apparently was for the packages Jaden carried in his wet suit, Jaden was a lot more anxious to get hold of some anti-itch **salve** and collapse in bed.

Hundreds, maybe even thousands of mosquito, yellow fly, and no-see-um bites **distended** the exposed skin on his arms, legs, and face. The salt water had **palliated** the itching for a while, but now the water had dried on his skin, adding to his misery.

Jaden hadn't even set foot on dry land when Squeeze **accosted** him. "Did you get the stuff?"

"Two words, Squeeze: *bug spray.*"

"Well?" Squeeze rocked on the balls of his feet.

"It's not an unrealistic **amenity** to expect. You could have warned me. Heck, for what I just went through, you could have thrown in a vial or two." Jaden unzipped his wet suit, revealing the

---

impetuous: impulsive
abort: cancel or stop
salve: remedy

distended: extended or swelled
palliated: reduced

accosted: approached challengingly
amenity: comfort or convenience

packets Squeeze was so antsy about.

"What's in these anyway?" Jaden asked as he handed the **penultimate** packet to Squeeze and withheld the last one for himself. He turned the waterproof white container around in his hand, considering it.

Squeeze snatched it from him. "Stuff." He quickly slipped it into his pocket. Now that his raggedy tuxedo bulged with packages from the U.Z., his normally oversize suit looked two sizes too small. "So, are you in love with a corpse?"

"I still don't know," Jaden said, letting the dealer change the subject. On the street, if someone didn't want you in their business, you stayed out—and stayed alive. "No leads except that she's either been fed to the gators or has set sail for some **arcane** raver paradise." Jaden scratched his already raw arms some more. "Of course she may have been carried off by mosquitoes." He sighed. At least he was too tired to worry about the bites keeping him up. "So you've got to send me back in. Soon, before something happens to her."

"Well, you returned alive, which is my most **pertinent prerequisite** for a runner—"

"I've got to know what happened to her," Jaden said. "Please."

"You're wound as tight as a perim guard on Internment Tuesday. You need a little . . . relaxer." He held out a small envelope. "It's on the house, for a job well done."

A rush of **sensuous** memories washed through Jaden's brain.

"I can give you a glow-key if you want to party—"

"No." Jaden seized the envelope and downed the little orange pill. If he couldn't be with Ally in the U.Z., he'd be with her now. "When am I going back in?"

"Tonight, if you don't score more Joy between now and then. And get some rest. Where you're going tonight, you're going to need it."

---

penultimate: second to last
arcane: mysterious or obscure

pertinent: relevant
prerequisite: necessary to an end

sensuous: gratifying the senses

Taking Joy alone, Jaden still felt the tenderness of his love for Ally, but without the music and the people, the real world crept in too completely, and he couldn't let himself go to just enjoy it. Dammit! He should have taken the glow-key from Squeeze when he had offered it.

Jaden spent his two hours of Joy flying **aerial** acrobatics along the northeastern boundary to the Unemployed Zone. Unlike the savanna where the ravers made camp, the area had some trees. He flew the sluggish Gull 200 below the designated flight path, seeing how long he could duck beneath the tree line before having to bob back up to avoid colliding with a sabal palm. His accident had made him **timorous** around the force field, but with Joy on his side, he felt invincible.

Ravenous and spent, he arrived at the barracks in Fort Miami just after the mess hall had closed. Figured. He crawled into his bunk without even bothering to take off his leave clothes and fell into a **fitful** sleep.

Bang! Bang! Bang!

"Get your **indolent** butt out on the parade ground, ripper!" a gruff voice hollered through the door.

Groggy, Jaden rolled out of bed. Wasn't it the weekend? He peered out the small window and saw the whole department completing a series of intense exercises on the parade ground. Ugh. Jaden threw on his gray workout uniform and dragged himself outside.

"Two circuits of the course and eight laps," Truck barked. "Best way to get the old blood pumping first thing in the morning!"

Jaden jogged half heartedly into the workout arena. He must

---

aerial: occurring in the air   **ravenous:** very hungry   **indolent:** lazy
timorous: timid   **fitful:** erratic or irregular

have left too early the day before and missed yesterday's session. After a **haphazard** attempt at stretches, Jaden tackled the course. Pull-ups were first. Two sets of bars were **juxtaposed**. Fotee, the medic who had worked on him the night of the crash, joined him, and before Jaden had finished ten, Fotee had done thirty and moved on to the next station.

Sit-ups were next. Fotee had finished before Jaden had even sat down. Each sit-up made Jaden want to heave. He was just not ready for this level of **strenuous** exercise after the night he'd had, topped off with those hours on Joy. Dirk slid into Fotee's slot and finished the thirty sit-ups before Jaden had hit the halfway mark.

At the push-ups slot, Reth slid next to him. Jaden couldn't let that jerk beat him out, no matter how poorly he felt. He forced himself to pick up the pace. If he didn't, he'd be **relegated** to last place and left working the course after everyone else had finished. His entire body itched and ached, and his head pounded—one of Joy's less joyous aftereffects—but somehow Jaden managed to make it twice around the course, **indefatigably** keeping up with Reth the entire way. By the time he had to do his laps, though, Reth had outdistanced him. Jaden still had two more laps when Reth finished and jogged over to talk to someone near the fence.

Dammit! If he had known about the stupid weekend drill, he never would have taken Joy so late at night. Stupid workouts.

As Jaden rounded the corner, he recognized the woman talking to Reth. It was Kim. He sprinted the last lap and jogged up to his old team leader.

"Kim! What are you doing here?" She was a welcome sight after such a **harrowing** week.

"Just stopped by to see how my boys were settling in," she said.

"It's rough," Jaden said honestly, "but it's worth the effort."

"It's a breeze," Reth said. "Never felt more alive. I can see why my father and grandfather both loved it here."

---

haphazard: random
juxtaposed: next to one another

strenuous: requiring energy
relegated: banished or assigned

indefatigably: without being tired
harrowing: tormenting

Kim nodded. "It's a noble path you're following. I'm glad you're fitting in."

Jaden hoped he was fitting in. The guys seemed nice enough, but he thought they were too **engrossed** in their jobs. But maybe he was the **anomaly** because he'd been so fragmented and scattered lately. He just had to get this Ally mess cleaned up, and then he could return his focus where it belonged, completely on his training as a ripper.

"How long are you staying?" Reth asked. "Maybe you and I could catch a bite or something."

"I've got a few errands to run in town while I'm down here. And I'm guessing you need a shower," she said, playfully pushing him away with one finger. "I'll look you up when I get back from town."

"Deal!" Reth said, bounding off toward the showers like a kid chasing an ice cream truck.

"I should really be going, too," Jaden said, running his fingers through his sweat-drenched dreads in hopes of keeping them out of his eyes.

"Not so fast, Ripper Emory. I thought I'd finally drag you away for that celebration meal," she said. She tossed her head and her long blonde hair slid down her back.

Jaden definitely wasn't in a **convivial** mood. "I thought you said you had errands."

"*You* are my errand." She smiled **enigmatically**. "And I won't take no for an answer."

Man, all Jaden wanted to do was sleep until his next **foray** into the Unemployed Zone after dark. But he'd put her off before. He couldn't get away with doing it again.

"Let me grab a quick shower," Jaden said.

"Don't take too long," Kim replied with a smile.

*   *   *   *   *

---

engrossed: completely engaged
anomaly: irregularity

convivial: enjoying food and company
enigmatically: mysteriously

foray: excursion

Jaden felt a little better after a shower, but he was still a bit **somnolent**. Kim picked a Caribbean-themed beach bar that sat directly on the Atlantic, and they sat sipping drinks with umbrellas in them.

"You're quiet," Kim said, **coyly** twisting a lock of her long blonde hair.

"Just **lethargic**."

"A lot has happened in the last week. You've got reason to be tired."

"Uh-huh . . . " Jaden muttered. He gazed out over the waves. The sea was a bit rough today. The waves on the east coast were nothing like those back home on the west coast of Tamlando. After traveling thousands of miles, east coast waves seemed to tower and crash **bombastically**. The west coast waves coming off the Gulf mostly snuck onto shore.

"We miss you back at the Splitting Center," Kim said. "It's not the same without you."

"It'll always be home to me," Jaden said.

"I haven't had a decent game of Groundhog's Day since you left."

Jaden frowned. "It's only been a few days," he said.

Kim glanced down at her lap. "It seems like ages," she almost whispered, "at least to me." She looked back up, her expression filled with intense emotion. "I miss you, Jaden Emory."

Jaden felt a twinge of discomfort at the way she said the words. He wasn't sure why, but suddenly things felt really strange between them. "I, uh, I miss you, too," he replied, his attention still drawn to the crashing waves behind Kim.

"Maybe I could come down once in a while, or you could come up. Would you like that?"

"Uh, yeah, sure Kim."

Kim sipped her drink. "Because you're not my employee anymore, so there's nothing stopping us."

"Uh-huh . . . " Jaden said, **mesmerized** by the waves.

---

somnolent: sleepy
coyly: playfully or coquettishly

lethargic: sluggish or slow
bombastically: in an overblown manner

mesmerized: spellbound or hypnotized

Suddenly Kim's whole face lit up. "You feel the same way, I knew it!" she blurted out. "I knew that once you got promoted and that girl was out of the way, things could be different between us."

Jaden blinked, the twinge morphing into a major knot in his gut. "Uh, wait, what are you talking about, Kim?"

"Nobody can object to us dating, now that you're a ripper."

"You and me?" Jaden gulped, his mind racing to process. Lately his life seemed to get more complicated by the second. "Uh, but Kim—you're my boss!"

"Not anymore—that's the whole point!"

"But, but still . . . isn't there some sort of rule against it anyway?" Jaden winced at how lame and awkward his words sounded.

The disappointment in Kim's perfectly made-up face was all too obvious, and Jaden realized he had some serious damage control to do. Dammit, why did Kim have to lay this on him when he was already dealing with more than he could handle?

Kim's expression turned from vulnerability to anger. "Some thanks I get for getting you the job of your dreams," she flung at him.

"Kim, that's not fair. I got the job because of my skills."

Kim laughed. "Is that what you think? If it makes you feel like a big man, then go ahead."

"You're saying I only got promoted because of *you*?"

"That was my job, to make sure you excelled."

"So I should date you to **compensate** you for doing your job?" Jaden hoped she would see the foolishness of this argument and back down.

"I wouldn't date you if you were the last man on earth!" No such luck, apparently.

"Hey, take it easy, Kim." Jaden strove unsuccessfully to calm her down.

"You jerk!"

---

compensate: pay

"I think you're being a little unreasonable."

"It's just so **onerous** to go out with me, is it?"

Jaden took a deep breath. "I didn't say that, it's just—"

"There are lots of men who would find me attractive."

"Kim, of course there are—you're hot," he began, figuring the best move now would be to find some way to placate her. "I just have too much respect for you is all."

"After all I've done for you, Jaden Emory," Kim said. "I can't believe you're treating me this way. What **effrontery**." She had seen right through his ploy.

"I just want us to be friends," Jaden pleaded. "Like we've been."

"After all the time I put in on you, you just want to be *friends*?"

Jaden's temper flared. "Hey, what am I—some broken-down clunker you **renovated**?"

"I thought of you more like a diamond in the rough—that with a little encouragement and assistance you might actually make something of your life and **aspire** to greatness."

"I am, Kim. I'm a ripper now. I'm making the best life I can."

"You used me," she said **vehemently**.

"*I* used *you*? You just told me that you were only nice to me because you wanted to date me!"

"Actually, I remember saying just now that I wouldn't date you if you were the last man on earth."

"Kim, what's happened to you? I don't get this—this *attitude*."

"Is that what you think I have? An attitude? You haven't seen anything yet."

As they rode in silence back to the fort, Jaden worried he'd made a **grievous** mistake in reacting to her proposition the way he had. He knew he didn't feel that way about Kim, but he could have handled it better. If he could **rescind** every thoughtless word he'd **uttered** he would. He tried to tell her so when they got out of the car.

"Kim, I'm sorry. I didn't think—"

---

onerous: burdensome
effrontery: shameless boldness
renovated: revived

aspire: seek to attain
vehemently: forcefully
grievous: serious or causing suffering

rescind: take back
uttered: spoken

Kim's hard **veneer** returned. "No, you didn't. Stay out of my way, Emory, if you know what's good for you."

He rested his hand on her shoulder. "Kim—"

She shrugged him away, her tone filled with **rancor**. "Get out of my face, ripper. You and I are no longer friends." She took off toward the barracks, leaving Jaden standing with his mouth **agape**.

---

veneer: superficial layer   **rancor:** bitter ill will   **agape:** wide open

Jaden had **resolved** not to think about Kim as he putted the speed-boat toward Key West with the sunset hanging off to his left, but the **tedious aquatic** journey gave him too much time to do just that. How had he **misconstrued** all the signals? He'd had no idea Kim had been **enamored** of him.

He kept replaying their conversation in his head, thinking of ways he could have kept the situation from escalating into such a heated argument.

Then he remembered something she'd said, something he'd almost forgotten with everything else going on. "Once that girl was out of the way. . . . " Had Kim manipulated him into pink-slipping Ally just so they could date?

No, it couldn't be. As **acrimonious** as Kim had been earlier, he couldn't believe that of her—he just couldn't.

One thing was certain, though. Jaden had made an enemy of his former **mentor**.

When the homing medallion glowed solid red, Jaden dropped anchor. Evidently the disgruntled boundary guard moved the opening before each trip so there wouldn't be any kind of pattern to be traced. For this **encore** trip, Squeeze had given specific directions about swimming quietly between the two small islands and then straight on to Key West, but the instructions were totally **extraneous**. Key West glowed **luridly** in front of him, a beacon in the early evening darkness. He was going to have a bit of a swim once he got on the other side of the force field, but it wouldn't be too bad with his motorized personal propulsion gauntlets, and at least the **briny** ocean meant he could stop searching for alligator bubbles this time.

---

resolved: decided
tedious: boring
aquatic: taking place in water
misconstrued: misunderstood

enamored: in love with
acrimonious: bitter
mentor: trusted counselor
encore: repeat appearance

extraneous: inessential
luridly: shockingly or with a red glow
briny: salty

Exhausted, Jaden **clambered** up the Mallory Square pier. In the shadows of the crumbling concrete pier, Jaden removed his flippers and scuba hood and tucked them in the bag he had brought along. Because it contained the contraband, Jaden kept the rest of the suit on. This time, though, he was smart enough to bring regular clothes to go over it. And bug spray, of course. He didn't know if Key West had giant mosquitoes like in the Everglades, but if they did, he'd be ready.

He pulled on khaki pants and a light, long-sleeved shirt. He concealed his ripper gear with a bandana wrapped around his head. He'd seasoned and weathered all the clothes before he left so that he wouldn't look like a store mannequin. Now, to find his contact.

He stole into the streets. The **garish** buildings oozed with people. In his classically unhelpful style, Squeeze had told him that his contact Mel was the floor boss for the Key West Casino and could be anywhere on the island. He hadn't even offered a description. Jaden was definitely on his own. He'd just have to scour the casino. But where to start?

A **cordial** brunette with curly hair piled high on her head called to him. "Hi, honey. Come on in and have some fun!" She wore a slinky dress split way up her thigh with tiny shells sewn onto the material, making her clink as she walked.

"I'm looking for the boss," Jaden said in his most **cajoling** voice. "Know where I can find him?"

"Who wants to know, honey?"

"A friend told me to look Mel up if I made it down this far," Jaden said **congenially**.

"Fresh meat, huh?" the girl asked.

"Yeah. Just got in." Jaden knew better than to **embellish** his story. From his years on the street he knew that the best lies were the simple ones, the ones that had some semblance of truth to them.

---

clambered: climbed awkwardly
garish: gaudy or brightly colored

cordial: gracious
cajoling: coaxing

congenially: pleasantly
embellish: enhance or add details

The girl slunk over to a burly guard and whispered something to him. The guard nodded and the girl **sashayed** back. "Earl will take you."

"Follow me," Earl grunted.

Earl led him through the **capacious** casino. An assortment of handmade gambling equipment covered every square inch. Almost everything was made of palm tree trunks, coconuts, shells, rocks, or driftwood. Every classic casino game seemed to be in play, from roulette wheels and cards to slot machines. The addicts all played calmly and relatively quietly, the only noise the occasional cry of "Jackpot!"

Jaden could handle this, at least. It was much better than **slogging** through a swamp filled with alligators and snakes and pirates. These people seemed to behave themselves. He was looking forward to a much easier transaction.

The bouncer Earl presented him to a short, balding, middle-aged man in a cream-colored suit and blue silk tie. "Boss, this guy's looking for you."

Jaden extended his hand. "I'm Jaden Emory, sir. Squeeze sent me."

A greasy smile resplendent with **avarice** oozed across the man's face as he shook Jaden's hand. "I'm Mel, the pit boss. This glorious establishment is my Key West Casino," he said, his arms swinging around. "Walk with me, Runner."

"It's quite an operation you've got here," Jaden said. "Very impressive."

"It is, isn't it?" Mel said **jubilantly**.

"How do you manage all of this?"

"Creative dedication. I love to gamble, and my patrons love to gamble," the **gregarious** man said. "It's the experience we relish, not the technology. We automate as much as we can, and what we can't, we handle manually. With enough manpower, we can do anything, and there's no **dearth** of that here in the Unemployed Zone."

---

sashayed: strutted ostentatiously	**avarice:** greed	**gregarious:** sociable
capacious: spacious	**jubilantly:** joyfully	**dearth:** scarcity
slogging: plodding heavily		

Mel swung by a blackjack table as a man won a hand with large stakes. The dealer gave him a nod, and Mel clapped the man on the shoulder. "Congratulations! How about some nice steaks on the house?" he asked, handing the man two slips of paper with a **grandiose** flair. "Stop by Margaritaville and they'll set you up."

The man beamed at Mel's **largesse**, but Jaden couldn't help but notice the **haggard** look in his eyes. People seemed happy, but as Jaden **canvassed** the casino, the closer he looked, the more vacant, drawn expressions he saw, eyes locked on the tumbling dice or the whirling roulette wheel.

"Care to try your luck, Runner?" Mel asked.

"I'm not much of a gambler, but thanks," Jaden said.

"Nonsense! Pick your poison. Everyone plays at the Key West Casino!" His **grandiloquence** boomed through the casino. "I want you to have a good time. I want everyone to have a good time!"

Somehow Mel's statement didn't induce a rush of joy and enthusiasm in his **hapless** patrons.

"I really just need to make my delivery and head back. I don't have anything to gamble with anyhow," Jaden said, still trying to sidestep the invitation.

"You've got your delivery," Mel said, arching an eyebrow.

"It's not mine to wager with."

"Come on, a little roulette or blackjack, double or nothing."

Jaden racked his brain for some way to **dissuade** the man. "I really can't. I just need to deliver and take your shipment back."

"I say you should gamble." Mel raised his voice to the crowd of gambling addicts in the casino. "What do you think, folks? Should he gamble?"

A general murmur of **concord** came from the players, more an **amalgamation** of mutterings than anything else.

"See? They all think you should do it."

Jaden shifted from one foot to the other. If Mel couldn't see the

---

grandiose: absurdly exaggerated
largesse: generosity
haggard: gaunt or wild looking

canvassed: examined in detail
grandiloquence: extravagance and pomposity
hapless: unlucky

dissuade: advise against
concord: agreement
amalgamation: mixture

discrepancy between his idea of all these happy customers and the actual despair they seemed to be in under the surface, he probably didn't have the firmest grasp on reality. "I can't, sir. It's not mine to gamble with."

The floor boss remained obstinate. "Possession is nine-tenths of the law, so they say. You're going to have to do it, Runner. In fact, I won't finalize the deal unless you do. You want to get paid, don't you?"

Jaden decided to try a more **canny** approach. "I could always take this stuff to Gaspar instead," he said, hoping that mentioning the competition might goad Mel to uphold his end of the bargain.

"That would be . . . unwise. You see, Runner, Gaspar may have some kind of **rapport** with your boss Squeeze, but I do not. If you don't gamble, I'll have to make a wager of you and let your boss find another mule."

Jaden gulped. "Make a wager of me?"

Mel nodded **emphatically**. "Oh, yes. A very creative one. Let's see, what should it be?" He rubbed his chin thoughtfully. "How long exactly do you think you can hold your head underwater in a tank filled with alligators?"

Jaden's face paled.

"Do you think your head will be torn off first, or will you drown before that? I've got to know how to handicap the betting. Such an interesting wager, don't you think?"

Jaden let out a resigned sigh, realizing there was no getting out of this. "If I gamble, what would I win?" he asked reluctantly.

"Ah, now that's the spirit! You'd get your life, of course, and the payment for the contraband."

"You agreed to pay to begin with."

"Jaden, my boy, we're criminals in here. You expect any of us to keep our word?"

"Then how do I know you'll **adhere** to your word *now*, even if I do what you're asking?"

---

discrepancy: disagreement
canny: clever or careful

rapport: harmonious relationship
emphatically: forcefully

adhere: stick

"I'm afraid you don't. But a wager won fairly is generally respected in my casino."

Great, so much for this being the easier of Jaden's two adventures. Now he had a real **conundrum**. He was obviously going to have to gamble, but he had to figure out some way to give himself the advantage. What game would he have the best chance at winning?

None. This was a casino, and considering its location, basically as corrupt a casino as they came. But there had to be something he could win. The automated games like slots and roulette were out. There was no chance they weren't fixed. Maybe something with cards, something where he was playing another person. He'd always been good at reading people, since he was a kid. Just because he had relied on The Corporation's cybernetics for so long didn't mean that he didn't still have his own talents. His experiences at the raves made that clear. Now if he only had some music. . . .

He surveyed the room but couldn't see anything helpful. "I don't have much choice, do I?" Jaden finally said.

"No, Runner, you don't."

"Fine. I'll do it, but only if I get to pick the game."

"Why, of course! My casino is your casino. Pick your poison."

"Blackjack."

"Blackjack it is, then." Mel clapped his hands. "Earl, the cards."

"I'm playing against you?" Jaden asked.

"Of course! You couldn't get me to sit this one out for anything."

Jaden didn't like the thought of trying to interface with Mel. The man was **savvy**. If Jaden reached out and tried to touch Mel's brain, he might feel the intrusion. But there was no way he'd win on his own. The man would inevitably be better at the game than Jaden was.

Earl brought a fresh deck of cards sealed with a seaweed band. A crowd formed around them, and murmurs of side wagers filled the casino.

---

conundrum: difficult problem

savvy: practical know-how

Jaden listened to the rhythm of the room, trying to turn the whispers into a flowing, **roiling** ballad.

Nothing.

Jaden reached out to Mel, focusing in on the sounds that the pit boss made himself—the even, calm breathing, the slight shift of anticipation as he shifted on his stool, the sound of his cards being set before him, the soft whisper of the card placed face down being slid up and revealed to its holder.

The colors radiated out from Mel. The colors became numbers, and Jaden saw a queen and a seven. Mel had a queen showing, so the face-down card had to be a seven.

Jaden peeked at his own face down card. A queen, and his face-up card was a seven.

Dammit! Had he just reached out into his own mind and gotten his own cards instead of his competitor's?

He tried to reach out to the deck of cards. Could he tell what the next card would be? If he took a card and he went over, he could bust.

An ace, a two and a five.

Now if he only knew the order. He'd have to take a card and see. If he and Mel had identical cards, he didn't think Mel would bow out gracefully. "Hit me," Jaden said.

Mel flipped another card for him. An ace.

"Hit me," Jaden repeated.

He got the two. Not much, but it would be enough.

"Stay," Jaden said.

"Hit me," Mel said with a **malevolent** grin.

His grin froze when he saw the five flip over.

"Twenty," Jaden said.

Mel shoved the cards across the table. "Let's just get this transaction completed."

A murmur of shock and surprise traveled through the casino.

Jaden wiped the sweat from his forehead. The bandana covering

---

roiling: turbulent or emotional   **malevolent:** evil

his cybernetics itched.

"This way," Earl said, leading Jaden away from the hubbub with an angry Mel several steps ahead. They took him to a secured room off the casino floor.

As Jaden unloaded his contraband from his wet suit, he summoned his courage. "Mel, you're a man in the know. I'm looking for a friend of mine in here." He told her about Ally and where Tail said she might be.

"No idea," Mel said **caustically**. "Raver fresh meat doesn't last long in here."

Earl handed Jaden the packages he was to take back and he repacked his wet suit.

"Earl will escort you back to the shore." He turned to the **burly** bouncer. "Make sure he's not followed." He looked back at Jaden. "You're not exactly **inconspicuous**."

"I thought I blended in pretty well," Jaden said, sniffing and wiping the sweat from his temples. His bandana shifted slightly and he readjusted it.

"What's wrong with your head?" Earl asked.

"Nothing."

Mel eyed him. "Take off that bandana."

"I'd rather not."

Earl snatched his bandana off, revealing the **burnished** metal plate on Jaden's head.

"Squeeze was stupid enough to send a ripper into the U.Z.?" Mel asked.

"Rippers get ripped," Earl growled, cracking his knuckles.

"We don't abide cheaters, ripper," Mel said.

"I didn't cheat!" Jaden lied.

"Rippers read minds," Earl said.

"I'm only a trainee, and I couldn't read anyone's mind even if I was a full ripper. It's not what we do."

---

caustically: bitingly
burly: husky

inconspicuous: not easily noticed

burnished: polished

He cocked his head at Earl. "You're dead, ripper," Mel said.

Earl lunged at Jaden.

Jaden ducked under his arm and bolted out of the room. He raced through the mass of slack-jawed gamblers in the casino, Earl and Mel in close pursuit.

"Stop him!" Mel shouted.

Jaden dashed through the front door, but the girl in the slinky gown stuck a high heel out and he went flying, landing on his face on the sidewalk. He scrambled up and raced into the crowd. Jaden faded into it, moving along with the thickening throng, despite the fact that it was generally moving up Duval Street, away from the ocean. He kept his head down and **affected** the swagger of a practiced partier. As he passed the first alley, he wobbled into it and ducked into the first darkened building he saw, hoping he had **eluded** his pursuers.

Unfortunately he wasn't alone. A group of well-dressed men bent over a soft light on a lab table, focusing intensely on whatever they had on that table.

"Earl's already been over to pick up the pills for the Runner," one of them said, without looking up. "Tell Mel the next batch won't be ready until day after tomorrow."

Jaden ducked his head and backed out of the warehouse. "Will do," he rumbled.

What the hell am I carrying? Jaden thought as he doubled back to the Mallory Square pier.

He didn't even bother taking off his street clothes before he slipped on his flippers and dove into the cold ocean and headed back for his boat. Too blasted close.

---

affected: influenced   **eluded:** escaped

The next morning Jaden tackled his workout with even less enthusiasm. To his surprise, he wasn't the last one to show up on the course. Jaden was halfway through his first circuit when Reth **ambled** toward the field.

He wasn't alone, though. Kim dripped from his arm.

At the fence, their **torrid** kiss drew catcalls from the other rippers, but neither blushed. Both seemed pretty pleased by their acquisitions—Reth obviously felt he'd taken something of Jaden's, and Kim was enjoying showing Jaden what he'd missed out on.

Jaden turned his back on the **amorous** couple and resumed his workout. Had Kim really felt so **aggrieved** that she had to spend the night with that cottonmouth Reth? What had Jaden done to her, really? A slight **rebuff** at worst.

Let the two of them have each other. Maybe they'd leave him alone so he could concentrate on finding Ally.

Behind him, more catcalls erupted.

*   *   *   *   *

Jaden knew Squeeze would be mad at him for not bringing the packages to him immediately, but after what Squeeze had put him through, he didn't care if the dealer had to wait or not. He had stored the packages in a locker in the parking garage. Jaden had to keep up pretenses with the rippers or he'd never be able to make another run for him at all.

Today was a particularly important day for Jaden. After months

---

ambled: walked in a leisurely way
torrid: scorching or passionate

amorous: in love
aggrieved: distressed

rebuff: brush off

of SimRipper, he was finally going to get a chance to do the real thing.

"For particularly **obdurate** addicts, we use the Hive," Truck said, pointing at the chairs encircling a pole. "Sometimes it takes more than one ripper to get all the evil out of a criminal. Makes it good for training purposes, too. A few of these joint sessions and you'll be ready to trade that gray uniform for a black one."

Jaden beamed. This was what he had been waiting for all this time. He really wanted to prove himself, to show that no matter what he had been or what Kim thought of him, he was **meritorious**—worthy of being part of the Ripper Squad. "I won't let you down, Sergeant," Jaden said.

"This guy's going to be worse than anyone you've ever dealt with before," Truck said. "He only wants to get ripped so he can be paroled from the Unemployed Zone. He'd never get out unless he got ripped, and he wouldn't survive his sentence in the U.Z."

"What did he do?" Jaden asked.

"Multiple homicide."

Jaden felt the blood drain from his face. He'd always hoped for a really **vile** criminal to treat, but was he ready for this?

Once Jaden, Reth, and six other full rippers were settled in the Hive, two guards brought the criminal in. He was a chillingly normal-looking man in his mid-thirties—blond hair, blue eyes, a high forehead that suggested a soon-to-be receding hairline. Nothing about his outward appearance that would reveal the hideous crimes he was capable of. And that was the great thing about ripping—at least soon this guy really would be as harmless as he looked. The guards secured the criminal to a pole in the center of the chairs and activated a force field.

"Let's just get this over with," the man said. "I've got a play date on the outside." He leered at the circle of rippers.

"They're really going to let this guy out?" Jaden whispered to Fotee next to him.

---

obdurate: stubborn   **meritorious:** deserving honor   **vile:** repulsive

"He'll be fine once we get done with him. Watch."

A collar unfolded itself from the pole and locked around the throat of the criminal. His eyes bulged as the ripper probe whirred into the base of the man's spinal column.

The room exploded with the colors of the addict's mind. His spirit was the sickly yellow of nicotine-stained fingers. Vile images oozed out of the man.

One by one, the rippers attacked the criminal's addiction, sniping out at him like a circle of cobras. Each ripper took a chunk, severing the evil from its source.

Jaden took his **venomous** nip. This was nothing like splitting, and nothing at all like SimRipper, even. Splitting **entailed** building a wall around the addiction. Ripping tore pieces out of the man, pieces that would never be replaced. And the pieces weren't just the man's addiction, Jaden saw now. The very process of ripping ensured that other pieces of the man might be removed. The need to sever the addiction totally from the man meant the process was less precise than splitting.

Still, the rhythm of the process **captivated** Jaden, and he found himself caught up in the precision teamwork of the group. The treatment took over an hour. When the collar was released, the criminal slumped to the floor.

"Is he all right?" Jaden asked.

"Now that we treated him, he will be," Fotee said.

"Who cares?" Reth asked. "If he dies, there will be one less criminal on the streets, reformed or not."

The other rippers laughed appreciatively.

Jaden thought that was a little extreme, but he was pleased that the **repulsive** creature would be a viable employee now. With the other bits they took out of him, he'd be **insipid** and perhaps a bit **obtuse** and not quite as sharp on the uptake, but The Corporation had a place for every employee. Jaden felt this knowledge run

---

venomous: poisoned or spiteful
entailed: involved

captivated: charmed
repulsive: arousing disgust

insipid: dull
obtuse: dull or stupid

through his mind, the words he'd heard over and over for years that had formed the whole new belief system that had helped him say goodbye to Amsterdam forever. It was reassuring to be back in this safe, mental place, remembering what his life was all about.

Being a ripper felt good, felt right, when he was with his department. Maybe being a ripper could even fill the hole left by Ally, over time.

Jaden couldn't help but get caught up in the celebratory mood of his teammates. They'd done a good job, together. For the first time in days Jaden felt good, like nothing could **sully** this moment.

Jaden turned to laugh at a joke Fotee had made when he bumped into a very serious figure in a blue suit.

"Sorry," Jaden began. "I—" His words stuck in his throat as he recognized one of the two twin auditors, then saw her twin standing next to her.

Her **impassive** face a slab of granite and her lips a firm line, the auditor closer to him spoke. "Ripper Jaden Emory, The Corporation has evidence that you are a music addict."

"*What?*" Jaden demanded, his body going cold.

"Come with us," the auditors said in unison.

Jaden followed them meekly into a windowless concrete room and sat when directed.

"I'm sure there's some kind of mistake," Jaden said.

"The mistake—" one auditor began.

"—is yours," the other one finished.

"I'm sorry, but I just don't understand," Jaden said. He wasn't a music addict, so that much would be easy to **plausibly** deny, but although he didn't know exactly what was in the packages he delivered between the Squeeze and the U.Z., he had most likely carried music cards and readers. Or maybe someone saw him leaving a rave. Man, this was going to be bad. It didn't matter if he was innocent or not. If they dug deep enough, there would be

---

sully: make dirty   **impassive:** showing no emotion   **plausibly:** believably

enough **circumstantial** evidence to convict him. He had to find out what they knew and what they didn't so he didn't confess to crimes they had no clue about. The best way to handle it would be to shut up and listen.

"An informant came forward," Auditor One said.

"And told us details of your recent **transgressions**," Auditor Two said. "It will go easier on you—"

"If you confess now," Auditor One finished.

Jaden laughed. "I appreciate the effort, but that trick only works in bad movies." To his **chagrin**, the trick had worked on him once, when he was seven and had eaten the remaining chocolate chip cookies. It didn't work any more. He wouldn't confess to anything just because they claimed they had the goods on him.

"The informant was quite specific," Auditor One said.

"The informant provided many details," Auditor Two added.

"Maybe you should share some of them with me, then, if you want me to confess." He folded his arms across his chest.

"Your position as a ripper is too high-profile. An internal investigation has been launched—"

"—to verify the details—"

"—prior to your arrest."

Jaden tasted bile in the back of his throat. Arrest? They were already planning to arrest him?

But the old street Jaden, Amsterdam-Ass Jaden, was not about to let these two suits bully him.

"So if you're not arresting me now, that means I'm free to go, then?"

"You will be watched," Auditor One said.

"Closely," Auditor Two added.

"If you decide to let me know what you're accusing me of, let me know. Until then, leave me alone," Jaden said, getting up and leaving the interrogation room.

---

circumstantial: related but inessential

transgressions: acts going beyond set limits

chagrin: humiliation or disappointment

Truck waited for him outside, as did the majority of the rest of his department.

"Emory, you're suspended," Truck said. "At least until the investigation results are in."

"But Sergeant!" Jaden exclaimed, "I didn't do anything! It's all just **speculative**."

"Then the investigation will vindicate you and you'll be back on the team. Until then, my hands are tied." Truck walked off down the hall, shaking his head.

"Bad form," Fotee said. "We all thought you were doing so well." There was sadness in his voice, regret.

"What a disappointment," another said.

"Great potential down the drain."

"Look, there's been a mistake," Jaden said, **denouncing** the claims. "I'm innocent."

The group was **implacable**. Nobody seemed to pay him any attention.

"I knew there was something wrong with him all along," Reth said conspiratorially. "He was always sneaking around back in Tamlando. He had to be up to something illicit."

"This is ridiculous," Jaden protested. "The only evidence they have against me is the word of some anonymous informant. You can't condemn me because of some faceless snitch."

"Your poor upbringing is what condemned you, ultimately. With a past like yours, you should have known you'd never amount to anything."

Jaden stiffened. He was tired of the **defamatory** comments, tired of having his past thrown back in his face all the time. "Back off, Warren."

Reth strutted around the small circle of rippers. "Ashamed of your life as a drug dealer?" Reth **chided**. "I would be too."

"Don't go there," Jaden growled. "You don't know anything about it."

---

speculative: inconclusive
denouncing: accusing

implacable: unstoppable
defamatory: causing distress

chided: scolded

"Oh, don't I? Poor little drug dealer kid rescued by The Corporation. Just couldn't stay away from the street addictions, huh?"

Jaden couldn't believe it. The only person who knew intimate details about his past was Kim. How could she be so **perfidious**?

A chilling thought grasped Jaden. Had she been the one to betray him to the auditors as well?

Jaden couldn't take it any more. All his hard work trying to rise above his tough past, all of it dashed on the rocks because of this loudmouth. He wasn't going to let Reth **debase** him any longer. **Catalyzed** into action, Jaden roared and tackled him **belligerently**. He caught Reth around his waist and dropped him to the ground.

Reth flipped him and landed a right cross on Jaden's chin.

Jaden felt strong arms pulling him and Reth apart.

"What the hell is going on here?" Truck's loud voice boomed from down the hall.

"He attacked me!" Reth squealed, rubbing the back of his head.

"We don't **condone** fighting here. Both of you, to quarters!"

Jaden pulled free of the arms that **inhibited** him. "You've all already convicted me before I've even had a trial." He stormed out of the building. If they were determined to make him a **pariah** and put him behind bars, he was going to stay free as long as he could.

What was he going to do? He'd be watched at every turn now. He couldn't get Squeeze his package, and there'd be no more journeys into the U.Z. for him. He needed help, but who was there left to trust? He was on his own. There was no doubt about that.

Baqer. Baqer would help.

Jaden still felt badly about the way things had been left between them, but he knew Baqer was a true friend. Jaden would be able to convince him to forgive him for being such a jerk at Ally's internment and help him out.

He rented another stupid flying car—a clunker—and headed to

---

perfidious: faithless
debase: corrupt or lower in status
catalyzed: brought about or inspired

belligerently: aggressively and angrily
condone: excuse

inhibited: restrained
pariah: outcast

Tamlando to see his only remaining friend. When he reached the Splitter Center lab, Baqer was putting equipment in boxes.

"Jaden, what are you doing here?" Baqer asked, shifting uncomfortably.

"Can we talk? You know, in private?" His meaning was **implicit** but he gestured at the drawer that held the security bypass switch just to make sure Baqer got it.

Baqer flipped the switch and nodded. "It's okay now."

"You've got to help me. I need to get a note to someone, but I know I'm being watched."

"Watched?"

Jaden noticed there was no sparkle in his friend's eye. Baqer usually relished the cloak-and-dagger stuff.

"Look, I know I behaved badly when we went to the internment at Fort Miami, but that wasn't me. It was the splitting. I had Ally split out of me, and it turned me into an **execrable**, unthinking corporate monster. I'm sorry, Baqer. I totally get why you'd **deplore** how I behaved. I should have told you sooner. In fact, there are a lot of things I should have told you." Jaden launched into a full explanation of the turmoil of his life, from having Ally split out of him to taking Joy to bring her back to infiltrating the U.Z. to look for her. "You're the only one I can trust, Baqer, my only friend. I'm sorry I didn't tell you this before."

Baqer's expression grew increasingly conflicted as Jaden spilled more of the story. He looked back down at his half-packed box, clearly torn. "Jaden, I—"

"Look, I wouldn't ask you to help if I had any other options. With these auditors watching every move I make, I can't ever go back into the U.Z., and I definitely can't go see Squeeze. I hate to ask you to be **complicit** in my affairs again, but I need you to get a note to him, to tell him what's happened." He pressed a folded note into Baqer's hand.

---

implicit: unexpressed
execrable: detestable or wretched

deplore: regret or lament

complicit: associated with a wrongful act

Baqer set it on the table and pushed it back toward Jaden.

"I can't."

"You always wanted some adventure, didn't you? Now's your chance, my friend."

"I can't help you," Baqer said. "I'm leaving. I—I finally got that transfer. I've got a three o'clock shuttle to New York."

"That's wonderful, but how? After all these years?"

"I just needed something to distinguish myself." Baqer winced as he said the words.

Jaden felt an uneasy ache as he finally noticed his friend had yet to meet his eyes.

"So . . . I showed Management the splitting device we created."

"Baqer, you didn't!"

"They were so impressed that they had me develop a version for rippers."

"You didn't tell them what I did—"

Finally, Baqer met his gaze. "I'm sorry," he said firmly. "I was tired of being here, not getting anywhere, and it seemed like you were turning into a whole different person, anyway. Crazy from the addiction you couldn't see, then crazy from the treatment for it. Not the Jaden I knew."

Jaden felt ill. Kim and Reth hadn't turned him in. Baqer had!

"How could you do this to me?" Jaden demanded. "I thought we were friends!"

"You **cherished** your addiction over our friendship."

Jaden couldn't believe his friend's betrayal. Not for one second had he ever doubted Baqer's **fidelity**. "But I couldn't help it," Jaden protested, panicked. "My addictions are part of me, of who I am." He paused, hearing his own words and feeling their meaning sink in. "Baqer, I didn't realize until I got split myself and then had the splitting negated by Joy that splitting doesn't just build a wall around the addiction like I thought it did. It

---

cherished: nurtured or appreciated

fidelity: faithfulness

walls away other things too, seals away part of who you are. Maybe—maybe splitting isn't always right." His mind reeled from all the epiphanies suddenly coming to him. Not until this moment, arguing with Baqer, had he understood that there was no way he could keep all his recent experiences with Ally and Joy separate from his life as a splitter and ripper.

He truly believed he and Ally should be free and together. And he also believed that having his feelings for her and everything else that made him who he was intact instead of split away was the way it should be. So then why did it make sense for the two of them, but no one else?

It was all he'd believed in for so long, but what if the Corporation was _wrong_? Jaden remembered being caught up in ripping that murderer, even as he saw all the other parts of the man they were ripping out of him for good. At the time, the experience had been a rush—it had felt like a job well done. But some nagging doubt inside of him had questioned the extent of the process even then, and now he realized why.

"I think you'd better leave," Baqer said.

"Yeah, I think so." Jaden turned and headed out of the lab, but he paused at the door. "You know, you once told me that The Corporation never forgave a betrayal. Seems they'll let you replace one betrayal for another."

*   *   *   *   *

Jaden moped defiantly into the mess hall on what he was certain would be his last day of freedom. Investigations never took long in The Corporation. It took a week to convict an addict. A preliminary investigation was bound to take far less time. He was certain the auditors would arrive with a judgment by the afternoon. Jaden sat alone at one of the tables.

Fotee walked up. "Visitor for you, Emory. Waiting for you in the ripping center."

As Jaden skulked to the office, he wondered who was waiting for him. Could Baqer have come to apologize? Or maybe Kim had realized that their five-year friendship wasn't worth throwing away over an attraction, and she'd come to help him out of this mess.

Jaden picked up his pace. It had to be Kim. Baqer would be in New York by now. It had to be Kim, here to save him.

He ran his card through the reader but the office door was already unlocked. It swung open with a light push.

There, flanked by two guards, was Ally Fayre.

"Ally! What are you doing here?" Jaden said, attempting to contain himself. After scouring the swamp for her he couldn't believe she could just show up at the center.

But something was wrong. The ebullient, glowing girl he had known on the outside had disappeared. Her blueberry-colored ponytails sagged, and dark brown roots crept through at her crown. She had her hands thrust in her pockets.

Her voice barely rose to a whisper. "Rip and release," she said.

"What?"

"Rip and release," she said louder. "I want you to rip me, to take this—" She pulled and plucked at her shirt with one hand while the other stayed buried in her pocket. "To take all of this evil out of my body."

Jaden wanted to wrap his arms around her, to comfort her, but what could he do with two U.Z. guards in the room?

He put on his most imperious voice. "I'll take it from here, men. She's not likely to overpower me." He winked. "Would you prefer to wait in the lobby, or should I call the guard house for pick-up when I'm done?"

One guard looked at the other quizzically. Maybe they had never been given a choice before. "Ummm . . . lobby," one said. The other nodded emphatically in accord.

Jaden waited anxiously for the guards to leave so Ally would relax and be her normal self again, but even after the door had shut behind them there was no change in her behavior. "Let's just get this over with," Ally said. "I want the evil out of me."

Jaden touched her chin and brought her face upward. "There's

---

quizzically: in puzzlement   accord: agreement

no evil inside of the girl I love, Ally Fayre."

Ally's aqua eyes were totally vacant. She pulled away from him and thrust her hand back in her pocket. "You just don't understand. I don't have any other choice."

"What happened to you, Ally?"

Her laugh was **acerbic**. "I got pink-slipped by the boy I loved. What do you think happened?"

"I can expl—"

"There is no way on earth you can explain away what you did to me. The only thing you can do now is make it up to me by ripping me so I'll no longer be Unemployed."

"You don't want that."

"How can you know what I want? You've never been inside the U.Z. You don't know what it's like. Even if my soul could bear the shame and **alienation** there's no way I'll live to see my release date twenty years out."

"Don't talk like that."

"Why not? It's the truth. But elite rippers don't have to think about the truth, do they?"

Jaden didn't even know where to begin. There was so much he wanted to tell her.

"I've been searching for you," Jaden said.

"From your cushy desk chair in Fort Miami?"

"I've been in the U.Z. twice now. I had to know you were okay."

Ally laughed derisively. "Nobody just waltzes into the Unemployed Zone."

"I didn't waltz. I swam."

She stared at him for a second, and the first flicker of life came into her features. "You're serious, aren't you?"

"Please believe me when I tell you _yes_ from the bottom of my heart."

Tears struggled down Ally's face. "Then why did you send me away?"

---

acerbic: acidic   **alienation:** emotional separation

"I'm as much of an addict as you are, but I didn't realize it at the time. Or maybe I did and just didn't want to deal with it. I had my addiction split out of me, but it changed me, took other parts with it."

"You're addicted? To what?"

"To you, Ally. I had you split out of me, and when I did, my world collapsed. I found **solace** in Joy, and it made me realize how wrong I had been."

Ally squeezed her eyes shut and shook her head in silence. "You're mocking me. I won't be **derided**."

"Ally, listen to me. It's true. It's all true."

"Ripping is the only way," she said, not opening her eyes. "Rip and release."

Jaden grabbed her by the shoulders. "Ally, snap out of it. That's just Corporation **propaganda** you're spouting."

"Rip and release," she repeated.

"I ripped someone once, a very evil man—a killer. It wasn't liberation for the monster—it was lobotomy."

"What?"

"Ripping doesn't just take away the bad parts of you. It takes away lots of little bits of you from all over. Once you're ripped, you're no longer the same person."

"I don't want to be the same person. I want to be different. I want out of the world I see with these eyes."

"I fell in love with those eyes, and the world they saw," Jaden argued.

"You only loved me when the music was in me," Ally said.

"That's not true!"

"But it is. The only time I'm who I truly am is when there's music. . . . " Her eyes got a dreamy, faraway look in them. "When there's music, the world explodes into color. All these beautiful shapes and colors swirl in front of my face. Without my music, the

---

solace: consolation   **derided:** made fun of   **propaganda:** ideas, facts, or information spread for a cause

world is variations on gray. I can't live like that."

Jaden's heart skipped a beat—Ally was a synesthete, just like him. But without the cybernetic implants, she had no way of controlling her experience.

"How long have you been like this?" Jaden asked.

"Forever, for as long as I can remember. And now I want it gone. If you rip me, maybe I'll forget the world has color."

"Ally, you've got synesthesia, just like me," he said eagerly. "You see music in colors and shapes. My cybernetics use music to turn people's personalities into what you see when you hear music. I used to think that my implants allowed me to help people, but I'm not so sure anymore. People's addictions are part of them, and even when they're split or ripped out, they're still with you. It's why Joy works so well. It only takes a small crack to let your addiction spark through.

"Don't you see? It's like my past. I've spent five years trying to forget the streets I came from, to pretend that the smart-aleck drug-dealer kid I was isn't still inside of me. But he is, Ally. He's part of me, and like your music, without my street smarts, I'm only a hollow shell."

"I don't want to be like this," Ally said. "I just want to forget it all."

"You'll never be whole until you accept who you truly are."

"And where exactly am I supposed to do that? In the Unemployed Zone?" Ally pulled her hand out of her pocket and held it up. She waved at him with four fingers.

Jaden gasped.

"They took my thumb, Jaden. They cut it off for a daily ration of stale meal bars and water." Tears rolled down her face. "I want to be ripped. Reprogram me or the only way I'll get out of the Unemployed Zone is when they scatter my ashes to the wind."

"I'll get you out of there," Jaden promised. "But you're going to have to go back in."

"Jaden, I can't. I just can't. There won't be anything left of me."

He grabbed a notepad from the desk and scribbled a note. "I want you to find a kid named Tail. Everyone knows him. Tell him to take you to see Gaspar—"

"Jaden, no! I haven't been in the U.Z. very long, but even *I* know who Gaspar is. He's a **despot** who eats ravers for lunch."

Jaden had seen that for himself, firsthand, but he had no choice but to **consign** her to someone's care or else she wouldn't be alive by the time his plan went into action. "Give him this note and wait there for me. I'll come for you in two days."

"Gaspar will be picking his teeth with my bones by then."

"Not if you give him this note. He may be **notorious** and he's definitely a mean bugger, but he's true to his word, especially if he thinks there's profit to be made. He'll give you **asylum**. Between Gaspar and Tail, you'll be protected. Just, uh, don't ever call Gaspar 'Don,' okay?"

"What?"

"Nothing." Jaden bit back a smile. Obviously Ally hadn't even heard the other name, which was better for her.

"Do you promise you'll come for me?" Ally asked.

"You have my word."

*   *   *   *   *

Jaden ate lunch at a synthetic-food cafeteria just off the base. He punched in the specs for the Cuban food he wanted synthesized, then **gorged** himself on chicken and yellow rice, crusty Cuban bread, and savory black beans, washing it all down with three cups of *café con leche*. It felt like the last supper of a dying man. And maybe it would be if he got caught doing what he **connived**.

Hopefully that wouldn't happen as long as he could identify, and lose, his tail. He knew he was being followed; the Corporation

---

despot: tyrant	**notorious:** famous in an bad	**gorged:** ate greedily
consign: commit	way	**connived:** conspired
	asylum: shelter or protection	

wouldn't allow a potential criminal out of their sight. But whoever they had sent to tail him must be good, because he didn't actually have any **empirical** evidence that anyone was around.

As he lingered over his meal, he noticed two brunettes in casual clothes talking in low whispers. Occasionally he'd catch one of them glancing his way. He had changed a lot in the past few months, but girls still tended to notice him.

He took another sip of his *café con leche*, continuing to watch the women out of the corner of his eye. They seemed a little old for him—he seriously doubted they were planning on trying to pick him up. Which meant . . . good possibility they were Corporation spies.

Both women were well-built and muscular. They wore tailored yet casual slacks and blouses, covered with blazers.

Then one of the women dropped her napkin. When she reached down to pick it up, her blazer fell open, revealing a small yet lethal blaster.

Bingo.

"Your flan, sir."

"I didn't order any—"

"I believe you did."

Jaden looked up and saw Squeeze holding a tray with an oval cup of custard.

"Yes, thanks," Jaden responded.

"And your bill, sir." Squeeze slipped a piece of paper face down onto the table and walked away.

Jaden picked up the slip of paper. *Bathroom. Now.*

Casually stretching, Jaden stood up and asked the nearest waiter where the restroom was, just loud enough to make sure the women had heard him.

At least that's one place where they can't follow me, Jaden thought.

Squeeze was waiting for him in the restroom. The door had barely

---

empirical: based on
observation or experience

swung closed behind Jaden when Squeeze grabbed him by the collar and shoved him up against the mirror. "What the hell did you do with my shipment?" he demanded.

"It's safe. I swear. But you saw, I'm being watched. I couldn't bring it to you."

Squeeze shoved him again and let go. "Ever hear of a freakin' phone?"

"Bugged, I'm sure."

"What the hell did you do to get yourself traced?"

Jaden told him everything, from his last trip into the U.Z. to storing the contraband in a locker in the parking garage, to the **accusations** of addiction and his promise to help Ally escape.

Squeeze leaned against the windowsill, his arms folded. His characteristic derby hat was missing. He wasn't himself at all.

"If you do get her out, just where are you two going to go where you won't be hunted down like dogs?"

"They won't even know she's gone. No one keeps track of people in the U.Z.—they're mostly worried about keeping them *out* of the civilized world."

"But they'll know when their **illustrious** little ripper is gone."

"I don't know all the details, but I promised Ally I'd get her out, and that's what I'm going to do."

"You won't stay out unless you've got a better plan than what you've got right now."

"I'll get Ally out, let them **apprehend** me, get put in the U.Z., give my thumb to someone, then escape from the U.Z. After that I'll be untraceable."

"Oh, brilliant. Because you don't need all ten fingers now, do you?"

"Squeeze, I don't know what else to do."

"You need a diversion."

"Like what?"

---

accusations: blame   **illustrious:** famous   **apprehend:** capture

"Like a whole bunch of escaped convicts. It's tougher to run down a couple dozen instead of just two."

"I can probably get Ally out without getting noticed, but how can I get two dozen hardened criminals out without them being noticed?"

"That's the point, goofus. You want them to be noticed. Let the cops run all over looking for a swarm of clever criminals while you and your little chippy scoot off the other way."

"But won't this ax any hopes you have of ever making another run into the U.Z.? Won't it get your guy in trouble if a whole bunch of criminals escape on his watch?"

"**Fractious** guy's been asking for more money. Can't stop paying him unless he's been silenced or else he'll give the whole operation away. I can always find another **licentious** night shift force field monitor with loose morals." Squeeze grinned. "Besides, it'll create the diversion I need to get my package back. With everyone out searching for you, I can slip right in and retrieve my property."

"What's in the packages anyhow?" Jaden asked, remembering the men he'd seen working over the lab table.

"You're so naïve. Joy, of course."

"Joy comes from the U.Z.? That's impossible."

"You've seen the facilities some of the warlords have. Where do you think Gaspar got his airboats or Mel got his roulette wheel? They export Joy, and I export the things they require to feed the need."

"But why not just make it out here? Sneaking into the U.Z. is risky and, believe me—far from easy."

"And so is having your operation found out by the cops. Nobody polices the U.Z., so nobody notices."

"And you trust criminals to make the drugs?"

"In case you haven't noticed, Amsterdam, we *are* the criminals. We're just the ones still on the outside."

---

fractious: unruly or irritable   **licentious:** immoral

Jaden knew Squeeze was right. Jaden was just as **culpable** as the addicts on the other side of the fence. He just had a bit more freedom.

Of course he wouldn't keep it unless he ditched his tail. And he couldn't stay in the restroom much longer without the women getting suspicious.

"I've got to get out of here," Jaden said.

"This way, so you're not followed," Squeeze said, indicating the bathroom window. "There's a small marina just south of Fort Myers. Your instructions will be waiting for you there, plus everything else you need."

"Thanks, Squeeze, for everything."

"How about a parting gift for the road?" Squeeze asked, offering him a small parchment envelope. "A little bit of Joy, on the house."

Jaden shook his head. "My joy is on the other side of that force field."

---

culpable: guilty

As the sun blazed in the afternoon sky, Jaden swam through the hole in the force field **encumbered** by a substantial bag. This time he was carrying not only his wet suit lined with contraband for Gaspar but also two dozen sets of breathing gear and force field homing medallions. His journey brought him back to the **desolate** Ten Thousand Islands region, a bit south of where he had entered before, so he kept a close eye out for pirates. Gaspar's men would be a welcome sight—well, as welcome as pirates could be—but since he wouldn't be able to recognize any of Gaspar's men besides maybe Mitch, it was best to keep a low profile.

He wasn't keen on swimming through the **brackish** water again, even with his personal propulsion gauntlets, but he didn't have much choice. He'd find the first **inhabited** island and see if he could steal a boat. At least he didn't have to manage it all in the dark this time. The outer boundaries of the U.Z. were so **ineptly** manned that even during the day the risk was minimal. And it was important to have as much time to escape under the cover of darkness as possible.

Ahead Jaden saw the first signs of life. A well-manicured island like something out of a fairy tale bobbed ahead. The grounds were **meticulous**. A walkway wound through the yard toward a white-washed clapboard-style two-story building. Each section of the board was painted with some sort of candy or sugary **confection**.

Jaden didn't see a boat, but maybe there'd be one around the back of the house. He noticed how quiet it was as the afternoon sun warmed the island. Who would live in such a quaint little house?

As if in answer, a heavy-set elderly woman with a **winsome** smile shuffled out the front door of the house. She wore her gray

encumbered: burdened
desolate: deserted or gloomy
brackish: salty or repulsive

inhabited: occupied
ineptly: awkwardly
meticulous: careful

confection: sweet food
winsome: charming

hair pinned in a tight bun on the top of her head and a loose gingham dress.

"Welcome to Candyland, young man," she said in a mollifying voice that reminded Jaden of his grandmother. "They call me Grammy Snapple." She held out a basket woven from palm fronds. "Would you like to sample an ice cold beverage?"

Jaden peered into the basket. Glistening with sweat, the ice-cold bottle called to him. He popped off the cap and let the sweet liquid pour over his tongue. "It's delicious," he said with **candor**.

"Why thank you, young man." Her eyes twinkled and the corners of her eyes turned up in **sanguine** wrinkles.

"You must have been in the U.Z. a long time," Jaden said.

"Oh, you'd be surprised. Not that long."

Jaden couldn't imagine what such a sweet little old lady had done to land herself in the Unemployed Zone. Based on her weight and the candy-themed decorations on her house, the best he could come up with was that she was an **insatiable** food addict. If only she had been able to say "no" to second helpings and her sweet tooth, this frail grandma would be back home rocking on her porch with her grandchildren on her knee.

"Grammy Snapple, I was wondering if you might have a boat I could borrow for the da—" Jaden's voice was cut short. It was as if his throat was shutting closed.

As darkness closed in around him, Grammy Snapple's beaming expression never wavered. "Didn't your mother ever tell you not to take candy from strangers?"

*　　*　　*　　*　　*

"Jaden, Jaden! Wake up!"

Jaden pried his eyes open. An anxious Tail stared down at him, snake-spearing stake in hand. The sun hung low on the horizon.

---

candor: forthrightness　　**sanguine:** cheerful　　**insatiable:** unable to be satisfied

He'd been out cold on the ground for several critical hours. Grammy Snapple was nowhere to be seen, nor was anyone else except Tail. "What . . . happened?" he croaked, his voice barely a whisper. Something was wrong with his voice, no doubt an aftereffect of Grammy Snapple's beverage.

"You tell me," Tail said. "When you didn't arrive when you were supposed to, Ally sent me looking for you. When I couldn't find you along the arranged route, I guessed that Grammy Snapple got you. She snags runners all the time."

"Is Ally . . . " Jaden found speech difficult. His throat felt as if a cat had used it to sharpen its claws.

"She's fine. She's with Gaspar. I'll take you to her."

Jaden suddenly realized he wasn't wearing his wet suit. "My bag, where is it?" Jaden forced out.

"What you see is what you get," Tail said. "I found you like this, just now."

Groggy, Jaden sat up. The world spun a bit before settling back on its normal course. Without the contraband and breathing devices, he was pretty much useless. Not only would he have nothing to give Gaspar for taking care of Ally, but he'd never be able to find his way out of the Unemployed Zone. He was stranded in the Unemployed Zone, with no way to escape, much less rescue Ally.

"We've got to get out of here before Grammy Snapple and her thugs return to Candyland. It won't take them long to fence your stuff."

Jaden **appraised** Tail. Was he telling the truth, or had the eleven-year-old stolen his stuff to sell to the highest bidder? The kid was the only one who knew how the homing medallion worked.

Tail dug in the small pouch at his waist. "Here, take this," he said, offering Jaden an amber drop about the size of his fingernail.

Jaden shook his head. He had learned his lesson about eating anything in this **forsaken** place.

---

appraised: considered   **forsaken:** abandoned

"Take it," Tail repeated. "It'll help you get your voice back."

Jaden held it between his thumb and forefinger. "What . . . is . . . it?"

"Pirate's gold." Tail's eyes sparkled. "We don't get much in the way of medicine in the U.Z. so some of us take this. It's got ginger and cinnamon, so it'll help with an upset stomach, a sore throat, or just about anything."

Jaden still eyed the **aromatic** drop suspiciously.

"Take it," Tail said. "It's my last piece."

Jaden hesitated. Whether he could trust Tail or not, the kid was his only ally out here. He didn't have much choice but to trust him, about the stupid cough drop or the bigger picture. Jaden took the lozenge in his mouth. Its spicy warmth **permeated** his throat as he sucked on it. He let Tail help him into the flat-bottomed boat and the eleven-year-old poled it away from the island.

They rode in silence as Jaden sucked on his drop of pirate's gold and waited for his voice to heal.

"So what's the plan, then?" Tail asked. "How are we getting out?"

Jaden's stomach sunk. "I don't know."

"What do you mean you don't know? What kind of rescue mission is it that doesn't have a plan for getting out?"

"I had two dozen breathing devices and homing medallions with me. Two dozen of us could have escaped. But they're gone now. Grammy Snapple took them."

"That's not good."

"That's an understatement."

"She and her men are probably already on the other side of the Unemployed Zone."

"I know," Jaden said despondently.

Tail poled faster. "If they're already out, there's a chance that they've already been discovered by the perims. If that's the case, they'll storm the U.Z. looking for the source of the **breach**."

Jaden put his head in his hands. What was he going to do?

---

aromatic: fragrant   **permeated:** spread through   **breach:** break or gap

"What are you going to tell Gaspar? He's waiting for the reward you promised him for taking care of Ally."

Jaden snapped his head up. He wasn't going to let this put him under. There had to be another way. "I'm not going to tell Gaspar anything. We'll sneak into the camp, take Ally, and leave."

"Leave for where? Without the equipment, we won't be able to get out of the U.Z., and inside the U.Z. there's no place Gaspar can't reach to find us."

"My boss will send help," Jaden said, not even convincing himself. Squeeze would not be sending help into the U.Z. and even if he did, he wouldn't be able to find them.

Tail arched a questioning eyebrow.

"Look, I can't just leave her there. If I don't get her out, when Gaspar realizes there's no payment coming, he'll kill her."

"I know."

"So let's just get her out of there and get as far away from Gaspar as we can."

"The Key West Casino might be **prudent**," Tail said. "Blaze was down there just the other day. Put Mel into such a tailspin that the place is still in an uproar. Turmoil makes for good hiding."

"Key West probably isn't the best idea," Jaden said. As they **disembarked** and hiked through the swamp, they swapped casino stories, and the two tales seemed oddly similar.

They neared the camp and Tail led them around to the less-patrolled edge.

"Wait a second," Jaden said. "You know, you don't have to do this. I can go in on my own. You're never going to be able to do business with Gaspar again if you help me. Maybe you and I should say goodbye here."

Tail grinned. "What, and miss out on the story of a lifetime?"

Jaden smiled. He was happy to have Tail with him. "Let's do this, then."

---

prudent: shrewd   **disembarked:** got out of a vehicle

Tail guided him silently around the perimeter of the camp to a hut on stilts. He pointed up the ladder and Jaden climbed.

Ally sat cross-legged in the middle of the empty hut.

"I've come to rescue you," Jaden whispered.

"You wasted your time," she said. "I'm not going anywhere."

"Ally, don't be ridiculous," Jaden whispered. "And keep your voice down."

"I can't go with you," Ally repeated. "We'll never be able to get out and even if we did, how could we survive in the free world, hunted like animals the rest of our lives?"

"Keep your voice down," Jaden hissed. He could hear Gaspar's men all around them. They moved with a nervous energy, as if something big was about to go down. It was only a matter of time before he, Ally, and Tail were discovered.

"Ally, I want you to do just one thing for me," Jaden whispered.

"What?"

"Trust me. Can you just please trust me that I'll find a way to make this work?"

Ally held her breath a moment, her eyes wide with fear. Finally, she nodded, breaking down in tears. "Oh, Jaden, I can't believe you're actually here," she said.

"Oh, Ally, this whole mess has been my fault from first to last. I—"

"Under the current **adverse** circumstances, I think it would be wise to forgo the *thank you for a lovely evening* crooning with our host," Tail said.

Ally cocked her head.

"Listen, Ally, the contraband I was supposed to bring to pay Gaspar for watching over you got stolen," Jaden explained. "We've got to leave now, before he realizes we're here."

"All right, Jaden. Let's do this—together."

"Ally, I—"

adverse: unfavorable or harmful

Gunshots erupted outside. Not just the little mini-lasers spread amid Gaspar's heavies. Jaden's trained ear picked up rifles and even a full-blown blaster cannon.

"Get down!" Tail hissed.

Jaden didn't know who was attacking Gaspar, and he didn't care. "Quick, we can slip out in the confusion."

Suddenly Gaspar himself ducked into the hut with his gun drawn, ready to protect Ally. Speechless, Gaspar's eyes narrow and he swiveled his gun to aim at Jaden.

"Traitor!" he shouted.

Gaspar's anger turned to shock and surprise as a red stain spread across his shirt. He crumpled to the floor.

Heavy black boots stepped over the pirate's body.

Reth strode into the hut, blaster drawn. His uniform was no longer trainee gray. It was the midnight black of a full-fledged ripper.

"You're both coming with me."

Coming up from behind, Tail knocked the blaster out of Reth's hand. Jaden tackled Reth, pinning him. Reth butted his nose with his forehead, and Jaden wheeled backward. Reth lunged for his blaster and reached it just before Tail did.

Reth grabbed the gun and then Tail. He took the eleven-year-old by his shirt and **hefted** him outside to navigate his way through the gunfire on his own. Jaden just hoped he could trust his instinct that Tail knew how to take care of himself by now.

Ally finally snapped to life. "He's just a kid!"

Reth snorted. "There's no such thing in the Unemployed Zone."

Weaponless and without any real choice, Jaden and Ally surrendered. Loaded up in the Raptor 300 that had rescued Jaden after his crash, he and Ally were returned to Fort Miami.

Instead of getting a speed-trial and sentenced into the Unemployed Zone, Jaden was taken back to his quarters, and Ally was whisked away toward the labs.

Jaden struggled to try to make sense of it all. What were they doing to Ally? What was going to happen to them? How could things have ever gotten this bad?

He heard a knock at the door.

"Come," Jaden said.

The door slid open and there, before Jaden, was Ally.

A rush of emotion flooded Jaden. He threw his arms around her and kissed her, dragging her into his room, but she was strangely limp in his arms.

Ally finally turned her head. The unmistakable kidney-shaped ripper implants gleamed.

---

hefted: hoisted or lifted

Jaden backed away. "Ally, what happened?"

"I'm a ripper now, just like you."

Ally no longer had blueberry-colored pigtails. Her hair had been dyed to match her roots and curved around her face in a flattering bob.

"Why did you let them do this to you?"

"What do you mean, *let them*?"

Jaden shivered. "How could you, after everything I told you about what splitting and ripping does to a person?"

"I used to think like you, too, but now that I've been through the procedure I see how silly that all is. You just don't have the proper mindset," Ally said. "I intend to use my new abilities to help people."

"Ally, no good can come of ripping, no matter how well-intentioned you are."

She remained **inexorable**. "You're so wrong. For the first time in my life, I know what my true role in The Corporation is. All these years of struggle and **angst** for what? If I had just come to The Corporation sooner, they could have helped me a long time ago."

"They're not helping you!" Jaden said, wishing he could be more **eloquent**. "They're changing you. They've made you someone you're not."

"And who are you to decide who I am? That's up to me, not you. For the first time in my life, I've got a talent all my own, something that defines me beyond my parents' wealth and status. If I use my powers for good, they can't help but be proud of me. They'll finally be forced to forget my **errant** past."

"There's no way, after everything we've done, that The Corporation is going to simply forgive and forget and let us **atone** and be productive employees again. They're not that **beneficent**," Jaden argued.

"You might be surprised," interjected a voice. And Jaden certainly was surprised to find Tail sticking his head through the door. The

---

inexorable: relentless	**eloquent:** vividly expressive	**atone:** make reparation
angst: anxious feeling	**errant:** making mistakes	**beneficent:** doing or producing good

kid entered the room. "They've been pretty beneficent to me."

Jaden was delighted to see him. "You made it out, Tail! But how? And what are you doing here?"

"Actually, after your crash, the Corporation paid me to keep tabs on you whenever you entered the U.Z. Some guy named Squeeze would tell them when and where you were entering, and I'd take it from there. They even promised they'd put me in the Splitter Academy if you got busted. So while it sucks to be you, I'm going to be a splitter now—pretty cool, huh, Ally?"

Ally and Tail high-fived.

Jaden rolled his eyes. "Listen, Tail. I really don't think you're going to like life as a splitter."

"As opposed to what—life in the swamps? I'm going to like it fine. When I get paid, I'm going to buy myself a Phoenix 5000."

Ally interjected. "Listen, Jaden. We're reformed. Like you were supposed to be. Only Tail and I aren't doing this half-assed, like you. If you're going to reform, you better go all the way—none of your hypocritical, cooler-than-thou posing, *Amsterdam*." She emphasized his nickname mockingly.

"Ally, I know you can 'reform' if you want to—but why would you want to?" Jaden knew there had to be some way of reaching her, of helping her remember who she was and what she stood for. "After all you've learned, do you really want to be an employee again? I know I don't. I'm not **contrite**, and I don't want to be."

"I know," Ally said. "That's why I'm here."

A chill crept over Jaden. "What do you mean?"

Ally locked the door as Tail stood watching, interested. From the small bag she carried with her, she pulled out a pronged device that looked like a tick.

Jaden backed away. It looked like the portable splitting device Baqer had invented, except it had been further developed . . . to be used for ripping.

---

contrite: sorry

Ally's expression was firm and passionless. "I'm here to help you, Jaden, just like you helped me. When I was at my lowest, you did what you had to, as a dutiful employee. You pink-slipped me so I could become one with The Corporation again."

"Ally—"

"But I'm going to save you the pain of the Unemployed Zone, and I'm going to let you keep all your fingers. That propensity you have for addiction, though—that's going to have to go." Her lips curled in a thin smile and her eyes flashed at him mockingly. "This won't hurt, Jaden. You may feel a slight . . . *pressure*."

SPARKNOTES®
TEST PREPARATION
GUIDES

The SparkNotes team figured it was time to cut standardized tests down to size. We've studied the tests for you, so that SparkNotes test prep guides are:

SMARTER

Packed with critical-thinking skills and test-
taking strategies that will improve your score.

BETTER

Fully up to date, covering all new features of the tests,
with study tips on every type of question.

FASTER

Our books cover exactly what you need to
know for the test. No more, no less.

SparkNotes The New SAT—Deluxe Internet Edition
SparkNotes The New ACT—Deluxe Internet Edition
SparkNotes SAT Verbal Workbook
SparkNotes SAT Math Workbook
SparkNotes SAT Subject Test: Biology—Deluxe Internet Edition
SparkNotes SAT Subject Test: Chemistry—Deluxe Internet Edition
SparkNotes SAT Subject Test: U.S. History—Deluxe Internet Edition
SparkNotes SAT Subject Test: Math Level 1—Deluxe Internet Edition
SparkNotes SAT Subject Test: Math Level 2—Deluxe Internet Edition
SparkNotes SAT Subject Test: Physics—Deluxe Internet Edition